THE DISTRIBUTION AND STAT
OF THE POLECAT *MUSTELA PUTORIUS*
IN BRITAIN IN THE 1990s

EDITORS:

J.D.S. BIRKS (1)

A.C. KITCHENER (2)

(1) The Vincent Wildlife Trust, 10 Lovat Lane, London EC3R 8DN
(Correspondence to The Vincent Wildlife Trust, 119 Church Street, Great Malvern, Worcs. WR14 2AJ)

(2) National Museums of Scotland, Chambers Street, Edinburgh EH1 1JF

Cover photograph: juvenile polecats – Bosbury, Herefordshire, July 1994.

TABLE OF CONTENTS

This report has been revised in the light of comments from several scientists and naturalists who kindly reviewed an earlier draft.

REFERENCING AND AUTHORSHIP OF SECTIONS

This report was written and edited by Dr. Johnny Birks and Dr. Andrew Kitchener. The document should be referenced as:

BIRKS, J.D.S. & KITCHENER, A.C. eds. (1999). The Distribution and Status of the Polecat *Mustela putorius* in Britain in the 1990s. The Vincent Wildlife Trust: London.

Each of the main results sections has been written as a discrete paper which may be referenced separately (see below). The following people are named as co-authors of certain sections because of their contributions to the collection and analysis of data and redrafting of the text:

Dr Angus Davison, Department of Genetics, Q.M.C., University of Nottingham, Nottingham NG7 2UM.

Miss Pauline Hanson, 54 Old Wyche Road, Malvern, Worcs. WR14 4EP.

Mr David Jermyn, The Vincent Wildlife Trust.

Dr Henry Schofield, The Vincent Wildlife Trust.

Dr Ken Walton, 17 Bryn Bras, Llanfairpwll, Anglesey LL61 5PX.

Separate referencing of individual sections of this report should adopt the following format, using Section 7 as an example:

KITCHENER, A.C., BIRKS, J.D.S. & DAVISON, A. (1999). Interactions between Polecats and Ferrets in Britain. pp. 84–110 in The Distribution and Status of the Polecat *Mustela putorius* in Britain in the 1990s. eds. J.D.S. Birks & A.C. Kitchener. The Vincent Wildlife Trust: London.

All uncredited photographs by Dr J.D.S. Birks.

1. SUMMARY

- This report presents the results of five years of survey and research work on the polecat *Mustela putorius* in Britain. The main sections include a review of previous distribution surveys, the findings of a new distribution survey by The Vincent Wildlife Trust (VWT) from 1993-1997, the development of a method for monitoring polecats, a summary of the relationship between polecats and feral ferrets, and a description of recent studies on polecat ecology in Britain. The work reveals that the polecat's recolonisation of its former range is continuing, and the report makes recommendations for conservation action.

- The polecat still has a restricted distribution in Britain due to past heavy persecution associated with game preservation in the late 19th century. Having been apparently common and widespread in 1800, its range was dramatically reduced to a main strong-hold in mid-Wales by 1915. The subsequent decline in persecution pressure was matched by anecdotal evidence of a slow recovery, although incidental mortality due to commercial rabbit trapping is believed to have limited populations until the mid-1950s.

- Organised distribution-mapping of the polecat on a 10km square basis began in the late 1950s. A series of published maps tracked the expansion of the polecat's range in Wales and the Welsh borders, from 93 10km squares occupied in 1962, to 245 in 1991. However, the rate of recorded range expansion declined after 1976, due probably to a reduction in recording effort. Notably, gamekeeping records from the 1980s suggest that distribution-mapping considerably underestimated the true extent of the polecat's range in the English Midlands at the time.

- A new polecat distribution survey was started by the VWT in 1993, based mainly on road casualty records. The main aim was to map the extent and pattern of recent range expansion outside the species' historical Welsh stronghold. Relatively little recording was carried out in Wales, where polecat distribution was better understood. Because of uncertainties about the relationship and distinction between polecats and feral ferrets, every effort was made to collect and examine specimens in order to validate records.

- The VWT survey produced 1,036 polecat records of which 44% were supported by direct examination of the animals. Road casualties comprised 68% of all records. Males outnumbered females by 2.4:1. A positive correlation was found between the length of 'A' class roads in 10km squares on the one hand, and both the number of records received and corpses examined on the other.

- Polecat records were received from 323 10km squares. 228 of these were new additions to the post-1950 distribution of the polecat. Combining these with data from previous surveys produces a cumulative total of 473 10km squares for 1997. This represents a 93% increase in the recorded extent of the species' range in Britain since 1991. However, some 70% of the apparent increase could be explained by the failure of previous recording to reflect the true extent of the polecat's expanding range. This includes the previously unmapped contribution of 87 10km squares occupied by new populations believed to have arisen from reintroductions since 1970. These populations now account for 18% of the 10km squares occupied by the polecat in Britain.

- In Wales the polecat is now well-established and widespread. However, it remains unrecorded from at least 17 10km squares in south Wales where road densities are high. The species is also still largely absent from Anglesey, though recent records confirm that it has begun to recolonise the island.

- The polecat now occupies more 10km squares in England than in Wales. It is firmly re-established in the English West Midlands, with a continuous distribution from the southern fringes of Manchester to south Gloucestershire, and from the Welsh borders to the Peak District, Northampton and Oxford. Beyond this naturally recolonised range, populations derived from reintroductions are established in Cumbria, the East Midlands and central southern England.

8

- In Scotland, a reintroduced population is established in the West Highlands. Further reintroductions are reported from the Highlands, but there is not yet sufficient evidence that populations have re-established themselves there.

- The eastward-moving 'front' at the edge of the polecat's range in the English Midlands is estimated to have advanced at between 3.5-4.3km per year since the mid-1970s. The principal reasons for this continuing recovery are believed to be reduced persecution and the increase in rabbit numbers (a favoured prey) following the growth of resistance to myxomatosis.

- Variations in the number of records received suggest that the polecat remains most well-established close to its historical Welsh stronghold. Geographical patterns in the factors likely to hinder polecat recovery (eg. high traffic density, intensive agriculture, persecution and use of certain pesticides) suggest that recolonisation is proceeding against a gradient of increasing negative pressures.

- In order to improve understanding of the polecat's recovery, a monitoring system based upon co-ordinated live-trapping by volunteers was developed and tested. 136 1km squares were each live-trapped for seven days within the species' current range in the mid-1990s.

- Significant regional variations in trapping success were recorded, and these were used to identify the 'current core' of the polecat's range. Trapping squares in the twelve 'core' vice-counties of Caernarvon, Denbigh, Flint, Chester, Merioneth, Montgomery, Salop, Cardigan, Carmarthen, Brecon, Radnor and Hereford were nearly twice as likely to catch polecats as those in the 13 remaining 'fringe' vice-counties (57% positive, compared with 31%). Where polecats were trapped in 'fringe' vice-counties they were apparently no less abundant than in the 'core', suggesting that differences between the 'core' and 'fringe' were due primarily to a greater patchiness of populations in the 'fringe'.

- No association was apparent between the numbers of polecats trapped and a wide range of habitat variables recorded in trapping squares. However, a positive association was apparent with estimates of rabbit abundance in sample squares. This association was strongest in the 'core' of the polecat's range, where the number of polecat captures was correlated with the number of active rabbit burrows counted in sample squares. In the 'fringe' of the polecat's range an inverse correlation was found between numbers of polecats and the density of main roads around sample squares. It was concluded that variations in the abundance of rabbits and the density of busy roads are significant influences upon polecat populations in Britain.

- Evaluation of the live-trapping system suggests that it could form the basis for a national polecat monitoring strategy. However, it has many limitations which must be recognised. In particular, the time and effort involved in trapping a 1km square for seven days, and the low trapping success (only 48.5% of squares trapped polecats), have implications for the involvement of volunteers, especially in the 'fringe' of the polecat's range where trapping success is lowest.

- The live-trapping data, combined with results from the new distribution survey, were used to create a new population estimate for the polecat in Britain. Population density estimates for the range 'core' and 'fringe' of, respectively, 101 and 69 polecats per 10km square were used to construct a minimum estimate of 38,381 for the whole British population. Separate estimates are presented for Wales (17,691), Scotland (483) and England (20,207). Notably these estimates suggest that polecats are now more numerous in England than in Wales.

- In order to resolve the apparent confusion over the relationship between polecats and ferrets, measurements were taken of corpses collected throughout Britain in the 1990s. Skins were given scores on each of ten features known to differ between polecats and ferrets. Linear measurements were made on skulls and cranial volume determined. Pelage (fur) scores showed clear differences between populations from different parts of the country, which enabled objective comparisons to be made with known Welsh polecats (these had the highest scores). Pelage scores decreased from west to east in Wales and England, which suggests that polecats have increasingly bred with ferrets as they recolonised England. Welsh-type polecats were confirmed throughout the existing Welsh and English Midland populations and in Cumbria and Argyll, with a variable proportion of ferret-like animals present in fringing and outlier populations. All animals from the Isle of Man, Shetland, the Western Isles, Mull and some parts of mainland Scotland were confirmed as feral ferrets.

● Complementary studies of mitochondrial DNA revealed that two geographically distinct lineages exist in British polecats and feral ferrets. One is confined to Wales and the English border counties, and is thought to be derived from the ancestral British polecat; the other is found throughout Britain and is thought to be derived from the domestic ferret. However, this genetic work indicates that polecats and ferrets are so closely related as to be regarded simply as two forms of the same species. Domestication in ferrets has involved selection against many of the predatory and survival skills found in wild polecats. As a consequence, the ferret phenotype carries competitive disadvantages in the feral state, so there is likely to be selection for the polecat phenotype in all wild populations. This is expected to limit the negative impact of introgression upon polecat populations in Britain.

● Basic information on polecat ecology was gathered through a radio-tracking study at two sites on farmland in the west of England. Mean home range size of males was 213ha, and for females was 125ha. Polecats were predominantly nocturnal, with 72.4% of all activity recorded during the hours of darkness. Activity in daylight was typically recorded from polecats underground in rabbit warrens, in farm buildings, or in thick cover. Radio-tracking data revealed that woodland edges, farm buildings and field boundaries were the most preferred habitats. In winter, farm buildings were the most preferred habitat; this association was explained by the polecat's predation upon farmyard rodents. A strong association was apparent between polecats and rabbit warrens. 49.5% of all radio fixes were recorded from such sites, and these comprised 80% of polecat daytime resting sites.

● A study of English polecat diet was carried out through analysis of stomach contents. Rabbits dominated the diet, occurring in 72% of stomachs which contained prey, and comprising 85% of the bulk of prey remains. Other prey inevitably made minor contributions, with amphibians being the second most abundant category recorded.

● The conservation implications of the polecat's close association with rabbits and farmyard rodents are considered. Maintaining healthy wild rabbit populations may be critical for polecat conservation on farmland where other prey are scarce. Non-target effects of agricultural pest control, notably accidental poisoning through ingestion of rodenticide-contaminated rats and mice, might have a serious effect upon polecat populations as the species spreads eastwards into areas of heavier rodenticide use.

● There is no evidence that continuing persecution has significantly hindered the polecat's recovery in the west of Britain. However, the accidental killing of polecats in tunnel traps is regrettable, is of doubtful legality, and could be minimised by the widespread adoption of an exclusion device. Such a precaution is important in view of the polecat's current spread towards areas of heavier predator control in connection with game shooting in southern and eastern England.

● Recommendations for conservation action and research are presented. Key conservation issues affecting polecats include road casualties, secondary rodenticide poisoning, the relationship with feral ferrets, low public awareness, ambiguous legal protection, deliberate and accidental persecution and habitat degradation. Recommendations for future monitoring and distribution-mapping are also made.

● The polecat's expanding range in Britain contrasts with its status elsewhere in its European range, where it is typically described as declining or of uncertain status. Its strong ecological association with rabbits in Britain also sets it apart from many other European countries, where it is typically associated with wetland habitats and prey.

2. ACKNOWLEDGEMENTS

The preparation of this report would not have been possible without the contributions of people who helped in many ways with the work that it describes. We are especially indebted to the many naturalists and members of the public who helped with live-trapping and took the trouble to collect polecat corpses. As far as possible, these contributors are acknowledged at the end of each of the main results chapters.

We thank Vincent Weir and the staff of the VWT for their support and encouragement throughout. We are grateful to many people for constructive discussion of polecat research and conservation issues during the course of our work, including David Bullock, Michael Clark, Russell Coope, Angus Davison, Steve Gibson, Mary Gough, Huw Griffiths, Noel King, Thierry Lodé, Robbie McDonald, Tony Mitchell-Jones, Mary Neale, James Packer, Justine Ragg, Johnathan Reynolds, Stewart Scull, Richard Shore, Paddy Sleeman, Steve Tapper, Roger Trout, Ken Walton and Derek Yalden. We thank Peter Creber for veterinary advice, and Derek Gow and Colin Fountain for access to captive animals for publicity material. We thank the staff of English Nature's Three Counties Team for their support.

We thank the following for reading and commenting on complete or partial drafts of this report: Henry Arnold, John Clarke, Angus Davison, Don Jefferies, John Martin, John Messenger, Richard Shore and Ken Walton. Their comments led to considerable improvements in the final version. We are especially indebted to Ken Walton for his help with redrafting Section 6.

Data for the polecat distribution dot-maps in this report were generated in DMAP[1].

JDSB gives special thanks to his wife Helen for her tolerance of interrupted nights, strange smells and surprising packages in the deep freeze, and to his dog 'Badger' for company in the field.

---

[1] DMAP, C/o Dr Alan Morton, Dept. of Biology, Imperial College, Ascot, Berks SL5 7PT, UK.

3. INTRODUCTION

J.D.S. Birks and A.C. Kitchener

This report presents the results of five years of conservation-led research and survey effort on the polecat (*Mustela putorius* Linnaeus, 1758) and its recovery in Britain, initiated by the VWT in 1993. Restoring carnivores to parts of their former range, whether through natural recovery or reintroductions, is fraught with difficulties (Yalden, 1993; Breitenmoser, 1998). The VWT's work has concentrated on addressing a range of scientific, practical and cultural issues raised by the polecat's recovery. Important elements of this work have involved collaboration with other organisations, notably the National Museums of Scotland (NMS), the Institute of Terrestrial Ecology (ITE), ADAS and the British Association for Shooting and Conservation (BASC). Some of this work has been published elsewhere (eg. Birks, 1993, 1997, 1998, in press; Shore *et al.*, 1996, in press 1999; Davison *et al.*, 1998, in press; Newton *et al.*, 1999; Packer & Birks, 1999). Where relevant, summaries of these published papers are included in this report.

The report concentrates on describing the distribution and status of the polecat in Britain in the 1990s. Following this Introduction, Section 4 sets the scene for this work by summarising the biology, recent history and previous distribution surveys of the species in Britain. Impetus for the VWT survey was provided by evidence that the polecat, which was still perceived as mainly confined to Wales, had become widespread in the English Midlands and elsewhere (Tapper, 1992; Birks, 1993). A period of active distribution-mapping was required and a new 1990s survey is described in Section 5. Section 6 explains the development of a systematic approach to monitoring polecats and considers some of the factors that influence variations in the species' abundance.

Recent perceptions of the status and distribution of the polecat in Britain have been confused by the occurrence of feral ferrets, and by limited understanding of both the relationships and distinctions between these two close relatives. Hybridisation between polecats and ferrets has also been identified as an area of conservation concern (Balharry *et al.*, 1994). Clarification of the taxonomic status, phenotypic and genotypic characteristics of and the degree of introgression in the wild between polecats and ferrets was urgently needed; these issues are addressed in Section 7. As an aid to understanding the current recovery of the species, some new information on the behaviour and ecology of the polecat in lowland England is presented in Section 8. Recommendations for conservation action for the polecat in Britain are outlined in Section 9.

It is intended that this report will improve understanding of one of the lesser-known British mammals. The polecat's recovery in Britain has much in common with those of the buzzard and red kite, yet awareness of the species and its status is very limited when compared with these birds of prey. The current lack of knowledge is unsurprising given the polecat's nocturnal habits, uncertainties surrounding its recognition and identity, its lack of distinctive field signs and, for most of the 20th century, its scarcity and restricted distribution in the far west of Britain where human population densities are relatively low. Prior to the VWT exercise there have been few scientific studies of the polecat in Britain. Notably, in the late 1950s Ken Walton initiated distribution surveys and research on the basic biology of the species (Walton, 1964, 1968a, 1968b, 1970); in the 1960s and 1970s Trevor Poole carried out laboratory-based behavioural work (eg. Poole, 1964, 1966, 1972, 1978); Philip Blandford undertook the first major field study of polecat behaviour in the 1980s, and wrote a comprehensive review of the species' biology (Blandford, 1986, 1987). In Europe the species is equally little studied and in many countries its status is uncertain.

Many people and organisations have helped with the work reported here, and their contributions are acknowledged at the end of each main section. A single reference list is presented in Section 10. A summary, by county, of the past and current status of the polecat is given in Appendix 1. The latin names of all species mentioned in the text are given in Appendix 2.

4. THE BACKGROUND TO THE VWT POLECAT SURVEY

J.D.S. Birks and A.C. Kitchener

4.1 A summary of polecat biology

Excellent reviews of polecat biology have been prepared by Blandford (1987) and Wolsan (1993). Though over ten years old, the former remains the most comprehensive and well-referenced review available in the English language; the following summary is largely extracted from it.

The European or western polecat is one of six mustelids native to Great Britain. In Europe its range extends from the Atlantic coast eastwards to the Urals, and from southern Scandinavia southwards to the Mediterranean and the Black Sea (see Figure 4.1). A closely related form, the eastern or steppe polecat, occupies the steppe and semi-desert zones further east. A third member of the wild polecat group, the black-footed ferret, occurs on the mainland of North America. The ferret is a domesticated polecat probably descended from the western polecat. The conservation implications of hybridisation between feral ferrets and wild polecats are outlined by Lynch (1995).

Figure 4.1. The distribution of the western polecat in Europe. Based on Blandford (1987), Mitchell-Jones *et al.* (1999) and the VWT Survey.

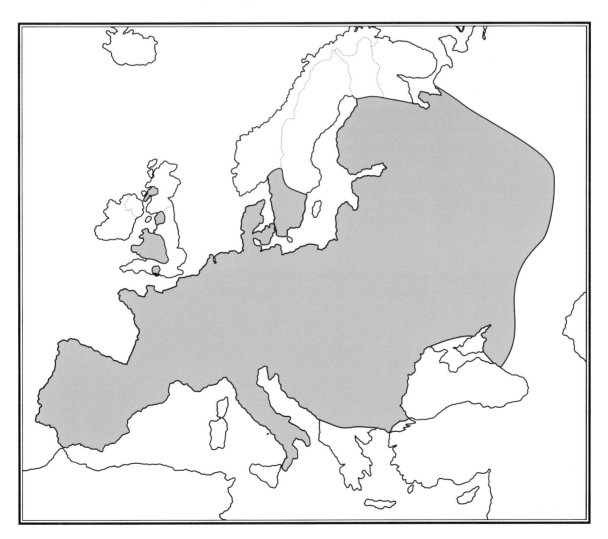

Plate 1. *Juvenile polecat aged approximately eight weeks, showing development of the facial 'mask' (Herefordshire, 1994).*

The European polecat is sexually dimorphic, with the larger males occasionally exceeding 60cm in length and 2kg in weight. The long, sinuous body shape and short legs are typical of the mustelid family. Very dark brown or purplish-black guard hairs overlie pale underfur to give the body a two-tone appearance, especially in winter pelage when the underfur is longest and thickest. The extremities of the body have grey underfur and, thus, appear darker. Visually, the polecat's most distinctive feature is the mask-like pattern of dark and light facial markings. Erythristic polecats are known to occur occasionally, in which the dark guard hairs are replaced by red ones. In France, Lodé (1994) has reported a significant incidence of 'dark' polecats which have little or no white fur on the face.

The name 'polecat' may be derived from the early French expression *poule-chat* (chicken-cat) - a reference to the animal's perceived pest status. The polecat's latin name *Mustela putorius* means 'foul-smelling musk bearer', referring to the pungent smell which the animal releases from paired anal glands as a defence when it is frightened or injured. This also explains the polecat's old English name 'foulmart', which distinguished it from the 'sweetmart' or pine marten which has no defensive 'stink'. The effectiveness of the polecat's anti-predator defence is illustrated by a recent encounter on Tregaron Bog in Cardiganshire, where two fit dogs, a collie and a black labrador, cornered an adult polecat on open ground with no cover nearby. The dogs attacked and attempted to kill the animal over a period of several minutes, but were repeatedly repelled by the polecat's powerful odour and sharp teeth and eventually gave up and left the animal unharmed; subsequently, the polecat's odour could be detected on the dogs' fur for several days (J. Davies, pers. comm.).

Adult polecats are normally silent, but they possess a variety of whickering threat and courtship calls, and may hiss and scream sharply when frightened. Polecats usually walk with an ambling gait, with the body stretched out and the head held low. Faster movement involves repeated arching of the back, giving the gait a sinuous appearance. Polecats hunt largely by hearing and smell, exploring burrows and other cavities, using their bodily flexibility to enter small openings. They are capable of short bursts of speed, and can jump and climb moderately well. Most activity is nocturnal, with little or no daytime activity except in mid-summer when breeding females may hunt both day and night to feed their young. Polecat resting sites vary from casual above-ground couches to (more typically) underground dens. The latter are usually existing cavities, such as rabbit burrows and holes

14

under trees, rockpiles and woodstacks, acquired opportunistically rather than self-excavated. Grass and leaves are often gathered from around the den to create a simple nest. In winter polecats may den in farm buildings and deserted outhouses where they prey upon commensal rodents (Birks, 1998). Typically, a polecat uses several dens within its home range.

The polecat occurs in a very wide range of habitats in Europe, including farmland, forests, scrub, mixed woodland, coastal dunes and cliffs, marshes and river valleys. However, most authors agree that it is less numerous at higher altitudes. Some describe it as preferring wetland habitats, and it is often associated with farmyards and farm buildings in winter. Polecats are almost completely carnivorous and the range of prey taken is broad. In Britain their diet includes shrews, voles, mice, rats, rabbits, hares, hedgehogs, small birds, poultry, young game birds, birds' eggs, frogs, toads, lizards, snakes; a range of invertebrates are taken, including beetles, bees, spiders, slugs, snails, earthworms and the larvae of flies and moths. Polecats are also believed to eat carrion, fruit and honey, and are occasionally reported to take fish in shallow water.

Lodé (1997) has recently reviewed dietary studies from 18 different populations across the polecat's European range. He concluded that the polecat is a generalist feeder with the flexibility to specialise on particular groups (notably rodents, lagomorphs and amphibians) where prey abundance permits. Polecat predation upon wetland prey, notably frogs and toads, is a particular feature of the species' behaviour in continental Europe, leading to suggestions that this may make polecats vulnerable to biomagnifying pollutants (Mason & Weber, 1990). In Britain, however, there is less evidence of an association with wetland habitats and no evidence of contamination of polecats with organochlorine residues (Jefferies, 1992).

Both sexes become sexually mature and are capable of breeding in the year following that of their birth. Testis growth starts in December and the weight of these organs remains at a peak between March and May. Females enter oestrus in late March or April, and mating is prolonged and vigorous, probably as a stimulus to induced ovulation. Unlike many other mustelids there is no delayed implantation; typically one litter per year of four to six young are born in late May/early June after a gestation of 42 days. Adult male polecats are not thought to play any part in rearing the young, indeed there is little or no evidence for a pair-bond between the parents. At about three weeks the young start to suck on solid food and their eyes open at five weeks. In Britain polecat 'families' consisting of mother and dependent young are first observed out of the nest in June or July. The young achieve independence from their mother at the age of two to three months, and usually disperse from their natal home range in September.

Polecats occupy individual home ranges, though there is some evidence that they are less strictly territorial than other small carnivores. In Wales, mean home range areas were 118.9ha for males and 28.8ha for females (Blandford, 1986) and in the west of England winter ranges were 180.4ha for males and 128.0ha for females (Birks, 1998). Population densities vary between 0.1 per km^2 in areas with fewest polecats to 0.5-1.3 per km^2 in the most densely populated areas (Weber, 1988; Birks, 1997). In Britain road casualties dominate data on polecat mortality. They are also killed by trapping and rodenticide poisoning. Some are killed by dogs and wild predators, but the polecat's defensive capabilities protect it from many such attacks. Polecats are especially prone to infestation by ticks, usually the hedgehog tick, which typically attaches to the head and interscapular region. They suffer from a range of other parasites, including the nematode *Skjrabingylus nasicola* which may cause death through abnormal bone growth. In parts of Europe a high incidence of rabies has been reported in wild polecats.

Polecat field signs are neither abundant nor diagnostic where feral ferrets are present. Polecat footprints often show only four of the five toes in prints which are typically 30 - 35mm long and 25-40mm wide on firm ground (on soft ground or in snow the hind prints may be 40-45mm long). In the commonest (bounding) gait the hind feet land close to or overlapping the front foot tracks. The stride length is typically 40-60cm depending upon the terrain and the speed and size of the animal. Polecat faeces (called scats) are up to 70mm

15

long and 5-9mm in diameter. They are cylindrical, twisted and taper to one end. They are usually blackish and musty-smelling when fresh, though the colour varies with diet. Like polecat tracks, scats cannot be distinguished from those of feral ferrets and are difficult to separate from those of feral mink. Polecat scats appear not to be used for scent-marking since they are usually deposited inconspicuously in a latrine associated with a den. Polecats normally consume their vertebrate prey by starting with the brain; otherwise their feeding signs are not especially distinctive.

4.2 The polecat in modern British culture

Early references to the polecat in British literature are wholly derogatory. In the 16th and 17th centuries the name 'polecat' was applied contemptuously to vile persons and prostitutes, as in Shakespeare's "Out of my doore you Witch, you Ragge, you Baggage, you Poulcat, you Runnion, out, out", Dekker and Webster's "To take their leaves of their London Polecats (their wenches I meane Sir)" and Day's "Hee's a male powl-cat; a meere heart-bloud soaker". Other references play upon the polecat's stinking reputation, as in Wolcott's "Brudenell, thou stinkest. Weasel, polecat, fly!", and Nashe's "With one Pol-cat perfume or another hee will poyson thee" (Simpson & Weiner, 1989). An echo of this appalling reputation survives today in the unflattering phrase "to stink like a polecat". Beyond this, however, the species has no significant place in rural or literary culture in Britain today.

This preoccupation with the polecat's stink probably derives from past human interactions with the species. Typically, most contact with polecats would have been in the context of persecution, involving animals held in painful traps or cornered by dogs. In such threatening situations the polecat's defensive odour would have been powerfully evident, leaving a lasting impression on those affected. Thus, the animal's distinctively pungent armoury has shaped human perceptions of the species, leaving it with an unsavoury image which lingers to the present day. Just as in the Middle Ages the polecat label has been used as a form of abuse in Britain, like the widely reported insult cast by a prominent opposition politician who referred in the early 1980s to one of Her Majesty's Government Ministers as a "semi-house-trained polecat".

During the VWT study intensive fieldwork on polecats was carried out in Herefordshire (see Section 8), where the rural community appeared unfamiliar with the species. However, there was limited evidence of a bizarre folklore developing. Two Herefordshire farmers independently stated that polecats were troublesome because they tended to chew the ears of sheep as they lay sleeping in the fields at night. Even more improbable was the statement, from two further independent sources in the west of England, that polecats were dangerous because they sprang up to bite grown men on the back of the neck, causing paralysis and death.

The portrait of two polecats on the front cover of a 1993 World Wide Fund for Nature calendar (Shields, 1993), a pub named 'The Polecat Inn' near Great Missenden in the Chilterns, and a fictional book about polecats leaving the Welsh mountains to seek a future further east (Guy, 1995) are rare examples of the representation of the species in contemporary popular British culture. The only recent, factual account of polecat biology in the popular hardback press is in Sleeman (1989), which also covers stoats, weasels and pine martens. This limited exposure contrasts with other carnivores such as the otter and badger, which are well-known and occupy prominent places in the nation's heart via their status as conservation icons, and through their roles in many popular stories. As a result, only 3.8% of rural schoolchildren within the polecat's English range could name the animal when shown a photograph, whereas 83.7% could name the otter (Birks, 1993). Interestingly, the word 'polecat' has been adopted by lighting engineers to describe a gadget used to secure a light in the angle of two walls, and as the name of a pop group!

Despite its unsavoury image and limited foothold in modern culture, the polecat does have some champions. There is evidence for developing support for the polecat among members of the ferret-keeping community, who are interested in the polecat as the presumed wild ancestor of their domestic stock. In addition, the recent focus by County Wildlife Trusts on biodiversity conservation has led to encouraging recognition of the polecat's significance as a recovering native species.

4.3 Current status of the polecat in continental Europe

Many authors have referred to the polecat's uncertain or unfavourable status in Europe. Evidence of recent declines in several parts of its range have prompted measures to protect the species within the European Union (EU), and this has shaped British legislation (see Section 4.4 below). Table 4.1 presents brief summaries of the polecat's status in a sample of countries within its European range.

Table 4.1. A summary of the polecat's status in a sample of continental European countries.

Country	Status	Reference
Italy	Status and distribution still poorly known; reduction in population and range reported in recent decades.	Vigna Taglianti (1988)
Spain	Status unknown, possibly declining due to habitat loss.	Blanco & Gonzalez (1992)
Portugal	Status and abundance unknown, though apparently widespread.	Santos Reis (1983)
Denmark	Declining since mid-1950s.	Jensen & Jensen (1972)
Belgium	Possibly declining.	Libois (1984)
France	Declining.	Saint-Girons *et al.* (1993)
Switzerland	Major 20th-century decline which has possibly halted; perhaps recovering in some areas.	Weber (1988)
Lithuania	Evidence of decline in numbers since 1960s.	Mickevicius & Baranauskas (1992)
Netherlands	Distribution stable, but numbers possibly declining.	Hollander & Van der Reest (1994)
Latvia	Population widespread, but sparse and possibly reduced. Status uncertain.	Ozolins & Pilats (1995)
Eastern Germany	Common and widespread, but population declining.	Stubbe & Stubbe (1994)
Luxembourg	Population declining. The least common mustelid apart from the otter.	Baghli *et al.* (1998), A. Baghli, pers. comm.

The reasons behind a fall in polecat numbers are often not well-known. Where authors have been tempted to speculate, they have tended to cite drainage of wetlands and loss of other habitats due to agricultural intensification (Eiberle, 1969; Jensen & Jensen, 1972; Blanco & Gonzalez, 1992). Conversely, where polecats have shown population increases or range expansions, these have been attributed to the extension of agriculture into forested areas (eg. Novikov, 1962). Both Walton (1970) and Blandford (1987) refer to recent extensions of the polecat's mainland European range. In northern areas this may be attributed to climatic amelioration leading to less severe winters.

4.4 Legislation relevant to polecat conservation in Britain

The polecat is listed in the Bern Convention, Appendix III, and in the EC Habitats and Species Directive, Annex V. These European measures place conservation obligations upon the British Government which are intended to be addressed through domestic legislation (see below). For example, Article 14 of the EC Habitats and Species Directive requires member states to ensure that the taking in the wild and exploitation of species such as the polecat "is compatible with their being maintained at a favourable conservation status". Following the 1992 Convention on Biological Diversity in Rio de Janeiro (commonly known as the "Rio Summit") the polecat is identified in the UK Biodiversity Action Plan (long list) as being of unfavourable conservation status in Europe (Anon., 1995). Although all such 'long' list species are classified as 'Species of Conservation Concern', they are of lower priority for conservation action than those on the 'short' and 'middle' list. Since the polecat does not qualify as one of these 'Priority Species', there are no plans to develop a Species Action Plan for it.

The polecat has received limited legal protection in Britain since 1982 following the passage of the Wildlife and Countryside Act 1981; it is listed on Schedule 6 of this Act and Schedule 3 of the Conservation (Natural Habitats etc.) Regulations 1994. These prohibit certain methods of taking or killing wild polecats. For example, whilst shooting with appropriate weapons is permitted, intentional trapping of polecats is prohibited without a licence. Section 11 (6) of the Wildlife and Countryside Act 1981 (as amended) requires anyone using traps to take "reasonable precautions to prevent injury thereby to any wild animals included in Schedule 6". Additionally, Regulation 41 of the Conservation (Natural Habitats, etc.) Regulations 1994 prohibits the use, for taking or killing protected mammals such as polecats, of "traps which are non-selective according to their principle or conditions of use". Furthermore, The Spring Traps Approval Order 1995 specifically excludes the use of spring traps for the capture of all species listed on Schedules 5 and 6 of the Wildlife and Countryside Act 1981.

Balharry et al. (1994) consider that, if ferrets are considered as the domestic form of the polecat, they would receive the same legal protection under the Wildlife and Countryside Act 1981.

In respect of polecats, none of the above legislation has been tested in a British law court, so it is difficult to assess its practical effect upon polecat conservation and management. Packer and Birks (1999) considered this issue and revealed that polecats are commonly killed in ways which are of doubtful legality. For example, it is common practice to catch and kill polecats in tunnel traps with practitioners relying on the uncertain assumption that the 'accidental' nature of such captures is a reasonable defence against prosecution. Legislative loopholes also exist. For example, whilst it is an offence to set a trap to catch a polecat without a licence under existing legislation, nothing in law apparently prevents the retention in captivity or deliberate shooting of any polecats (whether harmed or not) caught accidentally in traps.

4.5 Changes in the distribution and status of the polecat before 1950

Through the Middle Ages the polecat was persecuted as a pest and featured prominently in churchwardens' accounts which recorded bounties paid for vermin killed (Blandford, 1987). Polecats were regarded as a particular nuisance around managed rabbit warrens, and in the 16th century a trap called a hutch was used to catch them (Sheail, 1971). Despite this general persecution, available evidence points to the polecat being both widespread and common until the early 1800s (Langley & Yalden, 1977). Subsequently, however, there have been very considerable changes in the species' status and distribution.

18

4.5.1 The 19th-century decline

The scale and pattern of the polecat's decline in the late 1800s is documented by Langley and Yalden (1977) in their paper *The decline of the rarer carnivores in Great Britain during the nineteenth century*. Using such sources as the Victoria County Histories and published accounts by respected naturalists (eg. Forrest, 1907; Matheson, 1932), the authors compiled a table of probable extinction dates (or presumed survival) for the polecat in all British counties (reproduced here in Appendix 1), and constructed a retrospective series of distribution maps for 1800, 1850, 1880 and 1915 (see Figure 4.2). This evidence indicates a very severe contraction of the polecat's British range, with the greatest spate of county extinctions occurring in the period 1870-1910. The pattern of this decline is documented in detail in south-west Scotland by Ritchie (1920) using data on the price and numbers of polecat skins sold at the Dumfries Fur Fair.

In the view of Langley and Yalden (1977) the pattern of the polecat's decline, and that of the other two carnivores considered - the wildcat and the pine marten - "match very closely the development of the sporting estate, and the gamekeeping profession". The authors believed that, by the start of the First World War in 1914, "the polecat was apparently confined to the wilder parts of Sutherland, Ross-shire, Inverness-shire and North Argyll, if not actually extinct, in Scotland; to at most a few stragglers in the English counties of Herefordshire, Shropshire, Yorkshire and Cumberland; and to a stronghold in Wales of about 40 miles radius around Aberystwyth". It has since been suggested that an historical stronghold of some 70km (44 miles) radius centred on Aberdovey, some 15km north of Aberystwyth, is more accurate (Harris *et al.*, 1995).

Plate 2. *The upper Olchon Valley in west Herefordshire, showing the type of landscape in which the polecat survived outside Wales through the nadir of its late-19th/early 20th-century decline.*

4.5.2 Evidence of recovery early in the 20th century

During the First World War (1914-1918) gamekeeping pressure on the polecat was significantly reduced, leading quickly to evidence of a recovery in Wales. Langley and Yalden (1977) viewed this rapid response as important confirmation of their view that the polecat's decline was caused by persecution associated with gamekeeping. Several authors, writing in natural history and field sports journals in the early 1920s, commented on the continuing survival or, occasionally, increase of polecats in some parts of Wales and the

Figure 4.2. Distribution of the polecat in Britain in 1800, 1850, 1880 and 1915 (redrawn from Langley & Yalden, 1977).
Solid green shading – indicates common or widely distributed;
light green – indicates rare, declining or localised;
white – indicates extinct or data lacking, extinction presumed;
? – indicates status uncertain, but probably extinct.

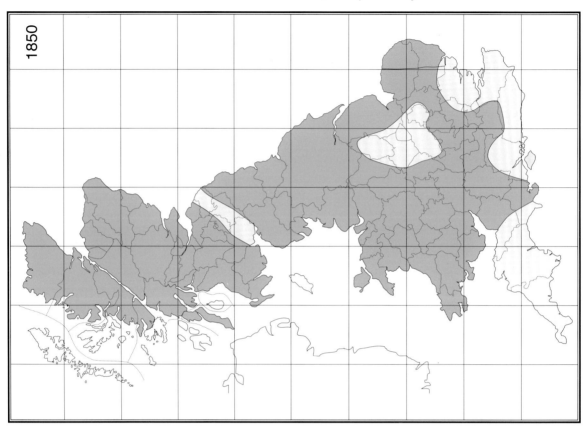

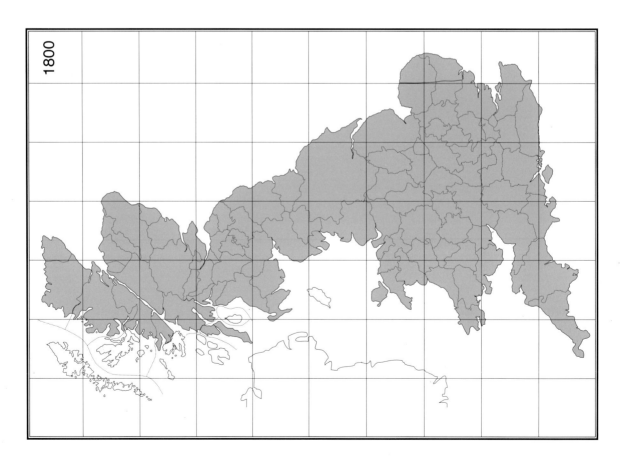

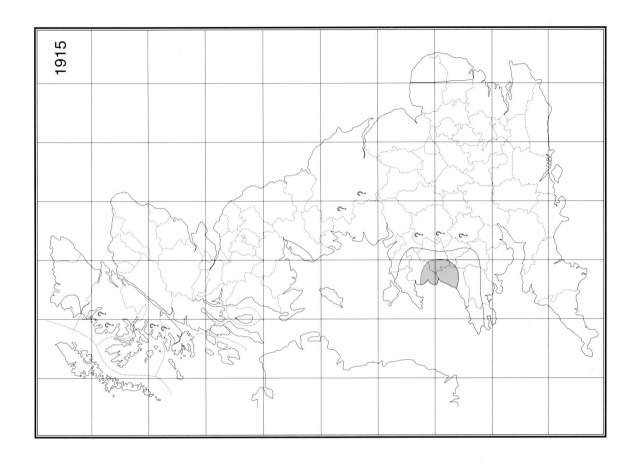

1915

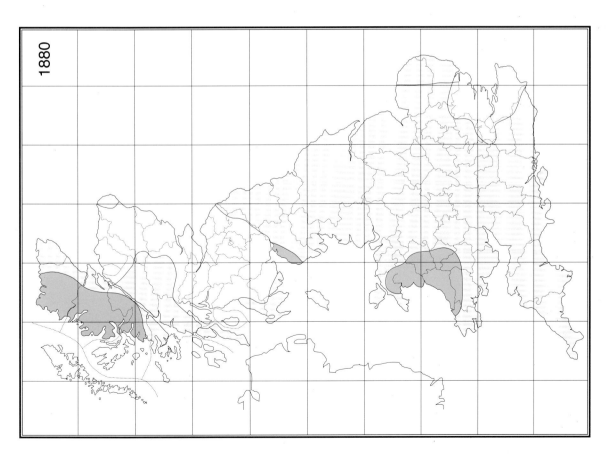

1880

21

English borders (eg. Forrest, 1921, 1923; Naish, 1923; Pitt, 1923). Nevertheless, it is clear from the comments of these and other writers that the polecat remained so scarce in the inter-war years (1918-1939) as to be worth remarking upon wherever naturalists encountered it. Some commentators were less than optimistic about the species' future. For example, Pitt (1921) wrote "In Britain the polecat is now rare, and is practically confined to central Wales. Any specimens found outside that area should be viewed with the gravest suspicion, generally proving to be merely escaped ferrets of a dark colour. The species still exists in some numbers in Cardiganshire, but how long it will be able to hold its own in the face of steady persecution is another matter".

4.5.3 Status in 1947-1950 (Taylor, 1952)

William Taylor of the Forestry Commission published what was probably the first systematic overview of the polecat's distribution in Wales (Taylor, 1952). He compiled a table indicating the status of the species over four years (1947-1950) in 51 areas administered by the Forestry Commission, only one of which was outside Wales, in Shropshire. This table is reproduced in Table 4.2.

Summarising the polecat's status, Taylor wrote "The species has undoubtedly profited by the reduced intensity of game preservation since 1914 and may be said to have taken a new lease of life, and the opportunity to increase its range, in most parts of the Principality with the exception of the county of Anglesey". He also described reports, from the Ministry of Agriculture and Fisheries Pest Officers, of the frequent capture of polecats in rabbit traps in the counties of Radnor and Brecknock, 25 having been killed on one farm in 1943.

4.6 Post-1950 recording undertaken before the VWT survey

Before the 1950s, information on the occurrence of polecats in Britain was in largely anecdotal form, making it difficult to document changes in the species' range and abundance with any certainty. Subsequently, however, a series of recording exercises based upon 10km squares was conducted. Some were specific surveys which appealed actively and widely for polecat records; others were passive in approach and depended upon the submission of records on an *ad hoc* basis with attendant deficiencies in coverage (Rich, 1998). Summaries of these surveys and a sample of distribution maps are presented below. Most have adopted a cumulative approach to distribution-mapping, based on the assumption that 10km squares recorded as positive in previous post-1950 surveys remained positive in subsequent surveys. In this respect there are some minor inconsistencies in the occurrence of positive squares between successive maps, but these do not detract significantly from the clear picture of steady range expansion.

4.6.1 1959-1962 (Walton, 1964)

The first proactive recording of polecat distribution, leading to a detailed, published distribution map, was conducted by Walton (1964). Starting in 1959, he appealed widely for reports of polecats, and stressed the need to avoid accidental inclusion of feral ferrets. Walton's criterion in this regard was the polecat's facial pattern which, where animals were available for inspection, "must resemble those described for *Putorius putorius anglicus* and *Putorius putorius putorius* by Pocock (1936)". The main sources of material were identified skins, animals seen and reported by trappers and others, and animals killed on the roads. During the four-year period 1959-1962, 312 records were accepted from 93 10km squares (see Figure 4.3). This survey revealed that polecats were confined to Wales and limited parts of the border counties of Shropshire, Herefordshire and Gloucestershire. Walton described the species as "common in the counties of Cardiganshire, Merionethshire, Montgomeryshire, Radnorshire, Caernarvonshire and south Denbighshire".

22

Table 4.2. Distribution and status of the polecat based on Forestry Commission forests in Wales, 1947-50, after Taylor (1952).

Forest	County	Status
Newborough	Anglesey	Not recorded
Beddgelert	Caernarvon	Not recorded
Gwydyr	Caernarvon	Rare
Clocaenog	Denbigh	Rare
Coed Clwyd	Denbigh	Rare
St Asaph	Flint	Not recorded
Hafod Fawr	Merioneth	Rare
Cynwyd	Merioneth	Not recorded
Coed y Brenin	Merioneth	Rare
Aberhirnant	Merioneth	Common
Dovey	Merioneth	Common
Dovey (Corris)	Merioneth	Common
Dyfnant	Montgomery	Common
Carno	Montgomery	Not recorded (but believed to be present)
Bryncynfil	Montgomery	Common
Commins Coch	Montgomery	Common
Hafren	Montgomery	Common
Kerry	Montgomery	Common
Mathrafel	Montgomery	Rare
Tarenig	Cardigan	Common
Myherin	Cardigan	Common
Cwmeinon	Cardigan	Rare
Brynmawr	Cardigan	Common
Radnor	Radnor	Rare
Coed Sarnan	Radnor	Rare
Brechfa	Carmarthen	Rare
Caio	Carmarthen	Not recorded
Crychan	Carmarthen	Not recorded
Brecon	Brecknock	Not recorded
Coed Caerdydd	Brecknock	Not recorded
Coed y Rhaiadr	Brecknock	Not recorded
Halfway	Brecknock	Not recorded
Glasfynydd	Brecknock	Not recorded
Hay	Brecknock	Not recorded
Mynydd Ddu	Brecknock	Not recorded
Usk	Brecknock	Common
Monmouth	Monmouth	Common
Tintern, north	Monmouth	Common
Tintern, central	Monmouth	Rare
Tintern, south	Monmouth	Not recorded
Itton	Monmouth	Rare
Chepstow	Monmouth	Not recorded
Goytre	Monmouth	Common
Llanover	Monmouth	Not recorded
Hencol	Glamorgan	Not recorded
Llantrisant	Glamorgan	Not recorded
Margam	Glamorgan	Not recorded
Penllegaer	Glamorgan	Not recorded
Rheola	Glamorgan	Not recorded
Slebech	Pembroke	Not recorded
Coed y Gocor	Shropshire	Rare

Figure 4.3. Changes in the recorded distribution of the polecat in Britain 1959-1991. See Section 4.6 for details of the surveys which generated these maps.

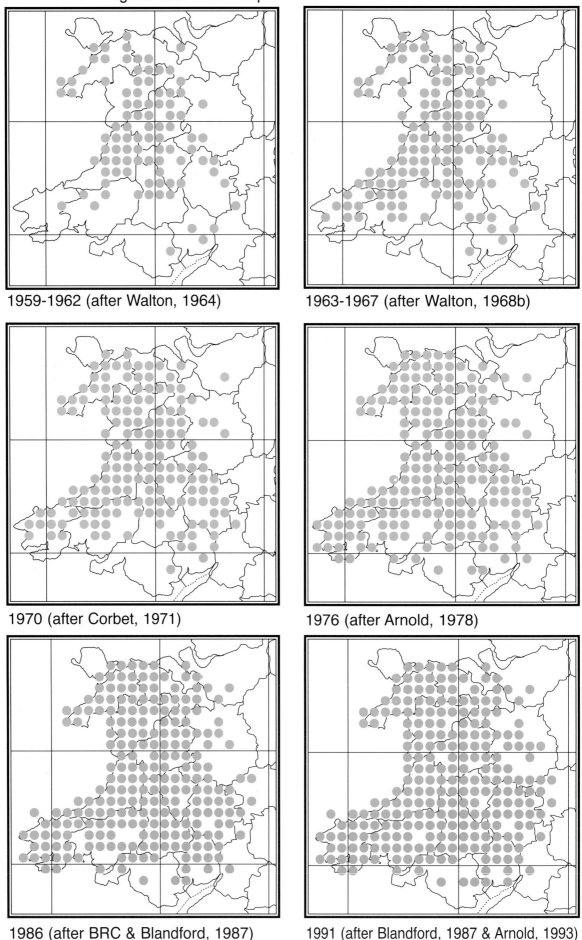

1959-1962 (after Walton, 1964)

1963-1967 (after Walton, 1968b)

1970 (after Corbet, 1971)

1976 (after Arnold, 1978)

1986 (after BRC & Blandford, 1987)

1991 (after Blandford, 1987 & Arnold, 1993)

Despite enquiries, Walton (1964) received no records of polecats from Anglesey, nor was conclusive evidence recovered from Scotland or any parts of England beyond the border counties named above. However, he acknowledged that a number of isolated occurrences of polecats were reported from elsewhere in England, but "in the absence of material evidence these have not been included, as it is possible that the animals in question were feral ferrets". Thus it seems that the small, relict polecat populations, identified by Langley and Yalden (1977) as surviving in Sutherland and Cumberland in 1915 (see Figure 4.2), had dwindled to extinction by the middle of the century. On the other hand the counties of Herefordshire and Shropshire, in which the polecat's status was uncertain in 1915 (Langley & Yalden, 1977; see Figure 4.2), appear to have retained the species.

4.6.2 1963-1967 (Walton, 1968b)

Using the same approach and criterion Walton (1968b) extended his initial survey (see Section 4.6.1) for a second period of five years. Almost 200 new records of polecats were added, and the published distribution map indicates that the polecat's known range had expanded by a further 42 10km squares, to a total of 135 since 1962 (see Figure 4.3). Much of this expansion involved a 'filling in' of previously vacant 10km squares within the polecat's main range in mid- and north Wales. However, Walton noted a marked range expansion in south-west Wales, with a more limited expansion also apparent in the south-east and north-east of the Principality. He accepted one sighting by a reliable observer (the late Ken Oxford) of a polecat on Anglesey - the first for several decades. In the absence of other records, this 1960s' animal is now believed to have been a "stray" (K. Walton, pers. comm.) and, writing later, Walton (1977) described the polecat as still absent from Anglesey. Commenting on the increasingly apparent recovery of the species Walton (1968b) noted that "the polecat is now present in many areas of Wales where it has never been within living memory", and "In central Wales it is now very common, particularly when compared with 10-15 years ago". However, the published distribution map showing individual records suggests that polecats were still absent from most of south Wales.

4.6.3 1970 (Corbet, 1971)

As part of an attempt to produce detailed distribution maps for all British mammals, initiated by The Mammal Society in 1965, Corbet's (1971) exercise relied very heavily on Walton's polecat records (see above). Nevertheless, by the end of 1970 Corbet's provisional distribution map showed the polecat's range as having expanded by a further 30 10km squares since 1967 to a total of 165 (see Figure 4.3). Much of this expansion involved further filling in within the species' main range in Wales, though significant extension into new areas was apparent in Cheshire, Shropshire, Herefordshire and Monmouthshire.

4.6.4 1976 (Arnold, 1978)

Continuing The Mammal Society's distribution-mapping, Arnold (1978) co-ordinated the production of a Provisional Atlas through the Biological Records Centre (BRC). Between 1970 and 1976 the polecat's range had expanded by 37 10km squares to a total of 202 (see Figure 4.3). This revealed a further significant expansion into south-west Wales.

4.6.5 1980 (Teall, 1982)

Reporting on a further phase of The Mammal Society's distribution-mapping, Teall (1982) produced a new distribution map for the polecat in 1980. 220 10km squares are recorded as occupied by the species in this survey, though at least five squares recorded as occupied in the earlier maps described above appear blank. Most of the newly occupied squares were in southern Wales and the English border counties.

4.6.6 1983 (Arnold, 1984)

Noting that some mammals were still badly under-recorded in Britain, Arnold (1984) produced a further set of BRC distribution maps as a stimulus to recorders. The polecat distribution map shows no significant range expansion compared with 1976 (see Section 4.6.4); indeed ten 10km squares which were positive in previous surveys appear blank in this 1983 map.

There is evidence to suggest that the polecat's true range in England in the early 1980s was more extensive than that shown by Arnold's (1984) distribution map. An analysis of gamekeeping records by Tapper (1992) revealed that estates which recorded polecats between 1981 and 1985 included several located 10-40km further east than the edge of the polecat's range shown in the BRC map for 1983 (Arnold, 1984). For example, Tapper's (1992) data indicate that in the early 1980s polecats were present in central parts of Staffordshire and Worcestershire, counties shown by Arnold (1984) as essentially unoccupied. Thus, it seems that some mapping exercises may have underestimated the extent of the polecat's expanding range. This is to be expected where resources do not permit an active and sustained appeal for records over and beyond the known range of the species. Furthermore, in view of the occurrence of feral polecat-ferrets, and the lack of familiarity with the subtle differences between these and true polecats among most naturalists (in England if not in Wales), there is likely to have been a reluctance among recorders to submit or accept records of polecats from new areas. Field guides have promoted this understandably cautious approach with conservative descriptions of the polecat's distribution as limited to Wales and a few border counties, and by urging that "records from outside this area need checking carefully because of confusion with feral ferrets" (Walton, 1977). Some publications compounded this problem by printing inaccurate drawings or photographs of polecats.

4.6.7 1986 (Blandford, 1987)

A further period of recording arose from the involvement of Blandford (1986, 1987) during his research on polecats in mid-Wales in the early 1980s. His distribution map for 1986 (Blandford, 1987; see Figure 4.3) indicates that the polecat's range covered 231 10km squares (an expansion of 29 squares over the 1976 range). Further eastward extension of the polecat's range was apparent from Blandford's records with new squares occupied in Cheshire, Shropshire, Herefordshire and Worcestershire. Encouragingly, Blandford's distribution map for 1986 approximates more closely to Tapper's (1992) for 1981-1985 (see Section 4.6.6 above). However, in contrast with Tapper's data Staffordshire is still shown as unoccupied.

Blandford (1987) commented that "we are witnessing a continuing recovery of polecat numbers, this stemming from a change in the 1950s in some vital factor in the polecat's ecology". He endorsed Walton's (1970) view that this change was the sudden decline in the use of non-specific 'gin traps' by professional rabbit-trappers, when myxomatosis so reduced rabbit numbers in 1954 that commercial trapping became uneconomical. However, Jefferies (1992) has suggested that the sharp decline in otters in Britain might also have been a significant spur to polecat recovery by reducing intraguild interference (see Section 5.4.1 for further discussion of this suggestion). Noting that polecats were still being killed in the interests of game preservation, Blandford (1987) suggested that "any further advance eastwards is unlikely to be rapid, given the pheasant rearing and vermin destruction which is prevalent in the English countryside". He also noted that there was new interest in reintroducing polecats in Britain and that successful reintroductions had already been made in Scotland (though the resulting populations were not shown on his 1986 distribution map).

4.6.8 1991 (Arnold, 1993)

Arnold (1993) concluded the collaborative BRC/Mammal Society distribution-mapping with the publication of an *Atlas of mammals in Britain*. The polecat distribution map showed 235 occupied 10km squares, though nine squares recorded by earlier authors as occupied (mainly Blandford, 1987) appear blank. A combination of the maps of Blandford (1987) and Arnold (1993) indicates a range occupying 245 10km squares. This represents an addition of 43 new squares in the 15 years since 1976 compared with 37 new squares added in the preceding six-year period 1970-1976 (see Section 4.6.4). Whether this decline in the rate of accretion of new squares can be explained by a reduction in recording effort, or by a genuine deceleration of polecat range expansion predicted by Blandford (1987), is debatable. It is perhaps significant that Staffordshire continued to appear unoccupied by polecats in 1991 despite evidence to the contrary from the early 1980s presented by Tapper (1992) (see Section 4.6.6). This contradiction, together with the indication that recent mammal recording effort had been limited (Arnold, 1993), suggests that the apparent decline in the rate of range expansion in the 1980s is an artefact of passive recording.

4.7 Variation in the apparent rate of range expansion up to 1991

Distribution maps based on passive recording cannot be expected accurately to reflect the true extent of the polecat's expanding range. Figure 4.4 shows how recording from 1980 onwards failed to keep pace with the rate of addition of new 10km squares that was evident in the 1960s and 1970s. If the higher rate at which squares were being added then had continued (7.8 new squares per year) one might have expected the range to cover 280 10km squares in 1986 (actual number 231), 319 in 1991 (actual number 245) and 366 by the end of the VWT distribution survey in 1997 (see Section 5). In practice, when a species is recovering from a decline the rate at which its range expands follows a sigmoid curve rather than a straight line, as was the case with the otter in Britain (Strachan & Jefferies, 1996). Thus, the true rate of polecat range expansion might have increased since the initial stages of recovery, assuming that habitat quality is comparable in the area of expansion, rather than having remained constant as the estimates given above suggest (see Section 5.3.4 for further discussion of this point). Since the accuracy of previous surveys is not reliable, it would be pointless to use them to calculate a recovery curve for the polecat in the way that has been possible for some other carnivores monitored in more reliable ways.

Figure 4.4. Rates of accretion of 10km squares to recorded polecat range by successive surveys.

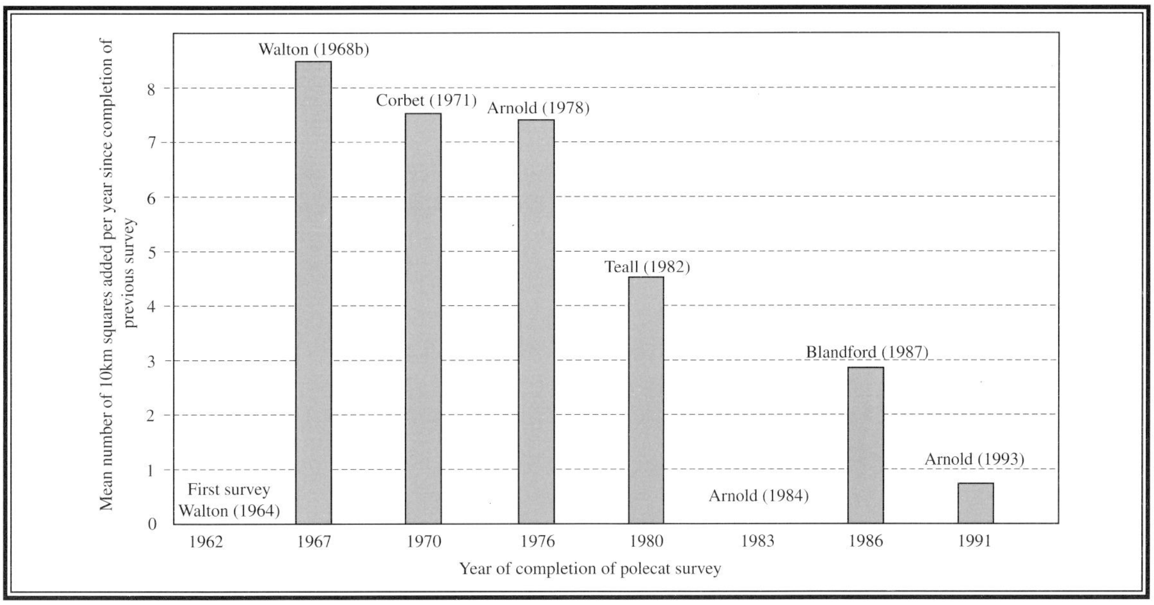

4.8 Acknowledgements

Thanks are due to Henry Arnold for provision of BRC data, and for helpful comments on an early draft of this section.

5. A SURVEY OF POLECAT DISTRIBUTION IN BRITAIN, 1993-1997

J.D.S. Birks

5.1 Introduction

Anecdotal evidence of the polecat's continuing spread (Birks, 1993), combined with suggestions that recent mapping exercises might have considerably underestimated the true extent of the species' distribution (see Section 4, and Tapper, 1992), indicated the need for improved recording in the 1990s. Furthermore, reports of new polecat populations becoming established, following reintroductions in both Scotland and England (Blandford, 1987; Birks, 1993), required proper evaluation. In 1993 the VWT launched a new phase of active polecat recording in Britain. The principle aim was to map the extent and pattern of recent range expansion outside the species' historical Welsh stronghold. Because of the need to commit time to other areas of polecat research, notably intensive fieldwork involving radio-tracking (see Section 8) and systematic live-trapping (see Section 6), and in view of the greater knowledge about the polecat's status in Wales, comparatively little effort was expended on simple distribution recording in the Principality.

5.2 Methods

Previous widescale polecat mapping exercises in Britain, reviewed in Section 4, have relied mainly upon the receipt of records submitted by interested naturalists. These have either been actively solicited through energetic appeals for information over relatively brief periods (eg. Walton, 1964; 1968b), or acquired rather more passively by longer-term recording schemes (eg. Arnold, 1993). Although Walton (1964) cautioned that recording should be conducted carefully in order to avoid the erroneous inclusion of feral ferrets, subsequent authors have not explained how they have addressed this problem. More limited distribution surveys have been based on records of polecats killed by gamekeepers (Tapper, 1992), and the use of questionnaires targeted at key sectors of the rural community (Taylor, 1952; Brown, 1989). Elsewhere in Europe scientists have typically based distribution and status surveys upon hunting statistics and trapper questionnaires (eg. Weber, 1988; Ozolins & Pilats, 1995; Baghli et al., 1998).

Contact with experienced naturalists in the English Midlands revealed that most were uncertain about the subtle differences between polecats and dark-coloured feral ferrets. This was quite understandable given the long absence of polecats from many Midland counties (often in excess of 100 years). This uncertainty has probably been compounded by illustrations in natural history and general publications of animals identified as 'polecats' which are clearly ferret hybrids (eg. field guides by Lawrence and Brown (1973) and Brown et al. (1984); articles in naturalists' (eg. Flack, 1994) and general interest magazines (eg. Aldiss, 1995); postcards by J. Arthur Dixon (ref. PWL 29300) and Dennis Print & Publishing (ref. G032081L); a video entitled *Night Hunters* by Stylus Video Ltd., 1989, re-issued by Survival Anglia Ltd., 1998). Furthermore, the general belief at the time was that the polecat was still mainly confined to Wales fuelled the perception that any polecat-like animal found some distance from Wales was most likely to be a polecat-ferret and, thus, was not worth recording. Conversely, feral ferrets and polecat-ferret hybrids were often identified as possible polecats. This 'ferret factor' was an important consideration in the collection and treatment of records in the VWT survey.

5.2.1 The aims of the VWT survey

The methodological approach of the VWT survey was driven by the simple aim of confirming the presence of wild polecats in the 1990s in the maximum number of 10km squares in any areas outside the species' well-recorded Welsh stronghold. Whilst the requirements of the VWT survey were broadly similar to those of previous exercises, there were grounds for applying greater rigour to the assessment of records received. This was especially important in view of the 'ferret factor' as a potential source of spurious records towards the fringes of the polecat's range (see Section 4.6.6). The lack of familiarity with polecats meant that mere reports of sightings could not be relied upon. Although most errors were believed to involve ferrets or polecat-ferret hybrids, two naturalists supplied fresh corpses of feral mink in the belief that they were polecats. Finally, experience showed that some genuine records received from far east of the Welsh border were met with such scepticism in some quarters that a considerable onus of proof was placed upon the administration of the VWT survey. This combination of factors demanded that this survey should maximise the proportion of records which were supported by unequivocal evidence. This was especially important towards the edge of the species' range and in the case of new populations arising from reintroductions.

5.2.2 The constraints

The polecat is largely nocturnal (Blandford & Walton, 1991a) and lives at relatively low population densities over most of its British range (Birks, 1997). As a result, live sightings of the species are too infrequent (and too uncertain, given the 'ferret factor' described above) to be relied upon for survey purposes. For example, during three years of fieldwork in Herefordshire and Worcestershire in the 1990s while driving at night, JDSB recorded only four chance sightings of live polecats on rural roads.

Indirect recording of elusive and uncommon mammals presents many difficulties. Nonetheless, effective methods have been developed and refined for some species. These have usually involved systematic searches for field signs in a predetermined sample of sites (eg. Strachan & Jefferies, 1996; Wilson et al., 1997). This approach is unsuitable in respect of the polecat, because its field signs are neither sufficiently abundant nor so distinctive as to be useful as the basis for systematic surveys. For example, a radio-tracking study carried out in the 1990s in parts of Herefordshire and Worcestershire where the species is well-established, revealed that possible polecat faeces and footprints were only rarely found in open countryside in the home ranges of radio-tagged individuals (see Section 8). The same was true of a widescale live-trapping study within the polecat's main range in England and Wales (see Section 6).

Even where polecat field signs are found, it may be impossible to distinguish them from those of closely related species. The polecat is morphologically so similar to the feral mink that both footprints and faeces of the two species are difficult to separate. Sidorovich (1994) has suggested that the footprints and track patterns of *Mustela putorius, M. lutreola* and *M. vison* can be separated in the field. However, he stresses that, depending upon the substrate, the distinctive features may not always be clearly expressed. This suggests that accurate field surveys by less skilled naturalists would be unreliable. It is even less likely that polecat field signs can be separated from those of escaped or feral ferrets, because the two are probably conspecific and morphologically identical in all relevant respects (see Section 7, and Blandford & Walton, 1991 a & b). Thus, the mere possibility of feral ferrets occurring can undermine any confidence in a survey based on field signs. Therefore, the biology of the polecat and its relatives prevents the establishment of simple, field sign-based distribution surveys; more importantly, it prevents the development of a systematic, repeatable monitoring scheme in which a standard approach and constant effort may be deployed at a large number of sites (eg. Strachan & Jefferies, 1996; Wilson et al., 1997).

Although polecats are trapped and/or killed as a result of predator control, generating valuable sources of data for game management organisations (eg. Tapper, 1992), those involved tend to be reticent about reporting such records to conservation organisations. This is understandable given the uncertainties surrounding the polecat's legal status (Packer &

Birks, 1999), and the public perception of the polecat as a scarce species deserving protection. Thus, direct and widespread access to records of polecats killed during predator control (a traditional source of information in Victorian times (eg. Langley & Yalden, 1977)) may be difficult for organisations such as the VWT, unless they can develop a trusting relationship with many individual gamekeepers countrywide. Even if this approach were feasible, the scarcity or complete absence of active gamekeepers in some areas, notably in the polecat's Welsh stronghold (Tapper, 1992), would place severe limitations on the value of this source of data.

5.2.3 The value of road casualties as a basis for distribution-mapping

Records gathered during previous attempts to map the distribution of polecats in Britain have been dominated by road casualties (Walton, 1968b; Arnold, 1993). This must be due in part to the constraints identified above, which limit the supply of other categories of records. However, there are aspects of the polecat's biology which are likely to contribute to this picture. Firstly, the polecat is predominantly a lowland species which, in hilly or mountainous areas where roads tend to follow narrow valley bottoms, may predispose it to road traffic accidents (Walton, 1968b). Secondly, aspects of the polecat's behaviour, including foraging for roadside carrion (Walton, quoted in Harris *et al.*, 1995), might contribute to its particular vulnerability to mortality on Britain's roads. This view was confirmed by a study in Wales, which revealed that polecats were the fourth commonest night-time roadside scavengers after cats, foxes and badgers (Slater, 1994). Finally, the pungent odour commonly emitted by polecats during violent death may lead to corpses remaining *in situ* and visible to recorders for many days, rather than being removed quickly by scavengers.

Walton (1970) proposed two further explanations for the surprisingly high incidence of road casualties. In Wales, certain stretches of road produced such concentrations of road casualty polecats that he suggested this may be due to the occurrence of highly favoured habitat either side of the road, leading the animals to cross roads much more frequently at these points. He also reported that polecat mothers tended to lead their young onto roads, where the animals seem to be unaware of the danger posed by oncoming vehicles, although adults occasionally take up a threatening posture. Thus, the polecat's biology probably conspires to generate a long-lasting source of road casualties wherever traffic densities are high enough.

There were further good reasons for basing the VWT survey on the recording of road casualties. Firstly, and most importantly, the collection of fresh corpses would permit simple assessment of phenotype, and would assist in the aim of validating the maximum number of records. Additionally, it would allow the establishment of a collection of contemporary polecat material for research (notably on diet, reproduction, taxonomy, genetics and toxicology). Also, the roadside corpses of an unfamiliar species were a suitably specific target for publicity, designed to involve the eyes and ears of amateur naturalists in a recording exercise. Finally, because the survey focused on the English Midlands, where road and traffic densities are high compared with those parts of Wales where previous recording efforts have been focused (Department of the Environment, Transport and the Regions (DETR), 1997), there were grounds for expecting a reasonable volume of road casualty records in areas where polecats were well-established.

Whilst road casualties were certain to be a valuable source of distributional data, many variables were likely to influence the probability of such records being received by the VWT. Notably these included the distribution and longevity of publicity, the variations in road and traffic density, the longevity of identifiable corpses, and the behaviour and activity patterns of potential recorders. These uncontrollable or immeasurable variables, considered by Slater (1994) in respect of wildlife recording generally, make it difficult to develop even a simple standardised approach to recording road casualty polecats. Inevitably they prevent the use of road casualty data as a basis for systematic monitoring, as opposed to simple distribution-mapping.

5.2.4 Publicity

The VWT survey depended on a sustained publicity campaign of unprecedented scale. Early in 1993 the VWT produced a poster (1,000 copies) and leaflet (20,000 copies) describing the polecat in Britain and appealing for records. Artwork and photographs explained the basic differences between polecats and ferret hybrids; the text encouraged people to collect and freeze corpses of any polecat-like animals before contacting the VWT. This publicity material was distributed widely within and beyond the polecat's known range, through a wide range of countryside organisations (notably the County Wildlife Trusts and County Museums).

Approximately 30 appeals for records, incorporated in articles written by VWT staff about the polecat's recovery, were broadcast through newsletters, journals and magazines published by local and national countryside and conservation organisations. In addition, over 80 illustrated talks were given to the memberships of such organisations and to the general public. These commonly led to further publicity via local radio, television and newspapers. Wider coverage was provided by national newspapers and magazines such as the *Weekend Telegraph* (Burton, 1993; Fewins, 1995), *The Daily Mail* (Davies & Porter, 1993), *The Times* (Hornsby, 1993), *Financial Times* (Woods, 1993), *The Observer* (Dunn, 1994), *The Independent* (Pugh, 1994), *The Countryman* (Birks, 1994), *Country Life* (Birks, 1995), and *Farmers' Weekly* (Gates, 1998). On 10th June 1993 the polecat's recovery was referred to in *The Archers*, a popular, long-running soap opera broadcast on BBC nationwide radio in Britain.

Little effort was invested in appealing for records of polecats in Wales, where the species was known to be widespread and well-established. At the end of 1996 the publicity effort was reduced. Subsequently, during 1997, effort was mainly invested in appealing for records from the fringes of the species' range. This included those parts of Wales where polecats remained scarce or absent, such as the south Wales valleys and Anglesey. The few records received after the end of 1997 are not included in the analyses and distribution maps presented in this section. However, where post-1997 records are especially significant they are mentioned in the text.

The survey benefited considerably from the efforts of many local naturalists who fulfilled an informal co-ordinating role in their 'patch'. They assisted with local appeals for records and with the collection of records and corpses. The appetite for good news in the field of nature conservation was such that many individuals and organisations were keen to become involved in monitoring and publicising the polecat's recovery (eg. Birks, 1992, 1996; Richardson, 1995; Gates, 1998).

5.2.5 Collection and handling of records

All records of possible polecats were collected and stored on a VWT database. Details of date, grid reference, name of recorder and the nature of the record were included, together with information on the appearance or, in the case of live sightings, the behaviour of each animal if this was available. The database was designed to export grid references to 'DMAP', a mapping programme which plots clear distribution maps. A simple distinction was made between those records relating to specimens examined by the VWT staff or their experienced collaborators, and those records where no specimen was available for examination. Many of the latter records were received in the form of letters or telephone calls about corpses or live animals seen. Where possible, these observers were interviewed about the appearance and behaviour of animals seen in order to identify records of obvious feral or escaped ferrets. Each record was classified according to whether it related to a phenotypically true polecat (see Section 7), an obvious ferret or hybrid or, in the case of specimens reported by inexperienced recorders but not examined by the VWT staff, an animal of uncertain identity. Although this survey started in 1993, in view of the recent lack of active recording of polecats in Britain (see Section 4.6.8), records originating from 1990 onwards were accepted.

5.2.6 Collection and treatment of polecat corpses

All polecat corpses supplied to the VWT were carefully examined and stored deep-frozen in 254 x 356mm 'seal again'[2] plastic bags. Date of collection, six figure grid reference, name of recorder and a record reference number were entered on 'write on panels' on the exterior of each bag. When receiving fresh corpses from naturalists or members of the public unfamiliar with the species, time was spent explaining the key points of distinction between true polecats and ferret hybrids. A geographically widespread sample of specimens was photographed in order to illustrate the appearance of polecats to those unfamiliar with them. The majority of specimens collected were subsequently donated to The Royal Museum of Scotland in Edinburgh, where material was processed for a range of collaborative studies under the supervision of ACK. One of these involved an assessment of pelage variation in British polecats (see Section 7).

5.2.7 Criteria applied in constructing distribution maps

In keeping with previous mapping exercises, and because of the minimal recording effort deployed in Wales, this survey adopted a cumulative approach to distribution-mapping. This meant that all 10km squares in which polecats were recorded by previous published surveys, starting with Walton's (1964) 1959-1962 survey, were classed as positive. This approach was believed to be reasonable in the light of the polecat's expanding range. As a precaution, contact was maintained with naturalists and mammal recorders in Wales to ensure that this did not involve false assumptions about the species' status.

Administrative boundaries within Britain have been subject to some reviews and reorganisations since 1950, posing problems for biological recorders wishing to use lasting and appropriate nomenclature and boundaries. In this report we have used two systems. In general descriptions of polecat distribution we have adopted the 'modern' county names (eg. Shropshire, Herefordshire, Gloucestershire, Cheshire) with which people are most familiar. However, wherever precision is essential in our accounts of polecat records, and in keeping with other recording organisations such as the Botanical Society of the British Isles, the system of Watsonian vice-counties (The Ray Society, 1969) is adopted in this report. Thus, the four 'modern' county names listed above are replaced in some contexts by Salop, Hereford, East Gloucester + West Gloucester (the two Gloucestershire vice-counties) and Chester. Figure 5.1 shows all vice-county names and boundaries. However, because Langley and Yalden (1977) used a different set of counties (those in place prior to the 1974 reorganisation) for their important review of the polecat's 19th-century decline, we have followed their nomenclature in Appendix 1.

All new records of possible polecats received during the VWT survey were stored on the VWT database. In view of the 'ferret factor', some discrimination was required prior to preparing new 10km square distribution maps. The following criteria were applied in England and Scotland when deciding whether a 10km square, not recorded as positive by previous surveys since 1950, should be classed as positive in the VWT survey:

- 10km squares which generated 'true' specimens examined by the VWT or its collaborators were classed as positive, except where these related to single specimens with no further records from the same or other squares within 20km (ie. no convincing evidence of an established population).

- 10km squares with one or more reports (not supported by specimens) of polecats, received from experienced and reliable observers known to the VWT, were classed as positive, provided these were not more than 10km distant from other positive squares.

- 10km squares with reports (not supported by specimens) received from observers not known to the VWT were not normally classed as positive unless they also generated more reliable records.

32

[2] Supplied by Transatlantic Plastics, Southampton, UK.

Figure 5.1. The Watsonian vice-counties of Great Britain (after The Ray Society,1969).

1. West Cornwall	24. Bucks	47. Montgomery	69. Westmorland	92. South Aberdeen
2. East Cornwall	25. East Suffolk	48. Merioneth	70. Cumberland	93. North Aberdeen
3. South Devon	26. West Suffolk	49. Caernarvon	71. Isle of Man	94. Banff
4. North Devon	27. East Norfolk	50. Denbigh	72. Dumfries	95. Elgin
5. South Somerset	28. West Norfolk	51. Flint	73. Kirkcudbright	96. Easterness
6. North Somerset	29. Cambridge	52. Anglesey	74. Wigtown	97. Westerness
7. North Wilts	30. Bedford	53. South Lincoln	75. Ayr	98. Main Argyll
8. South Wilts	31. Hunts	54. North Lincoln	76. Renfrew	99. Dunbarton
9. Dorset	32. Northampton	55. Leicester	77. Lanark	100. Clyde Isles
10. Isle of Wight	33. East Gloucester	56. Notts	78. Peebles	101. Kintyre
11. South Hants	34. West Gloucester	57. Derby	79. Selkirk	102. South Ebudes
12. North Hants	35. Monmouth	58. Chester	80. Roxburgh	103. Mid Ebudes
13. West Sussex	36. Hereford	59. South Lancaster	81. Berwick	104. North Ebudes
14. East Sussex	37. Worcester	60. West Lancaster	82. Haddington	105. West Ross
15. East Kent	38. Warwick	61. South-east York	83. Edinburgh	106. East Ross
16. West Kent	39. Stafford	62. North-east York	84. Linlithgow	107. East Sutherland
17. Surrey	40. Salop	63. South-west York	85. Fife	108. West Sutherland
18. South Essex	41. Glamorgan	64. Mid-west York	86. Stirling	109. Caithness
19. North Essex	42. Brecon	65. North-west York	87. West Perth	110. Outer Hebrides
20. Herts	43. Radnor	66. Durham	88. Mid Perth	
21. Middlesex	44. Carmarthen	67. Northumberland South	89. East Perth	
22. Berks	45. Pembroke		90. Forfar	
23. Oxford	46. Cardigan	68. Cheviotland	91. Kincardine	

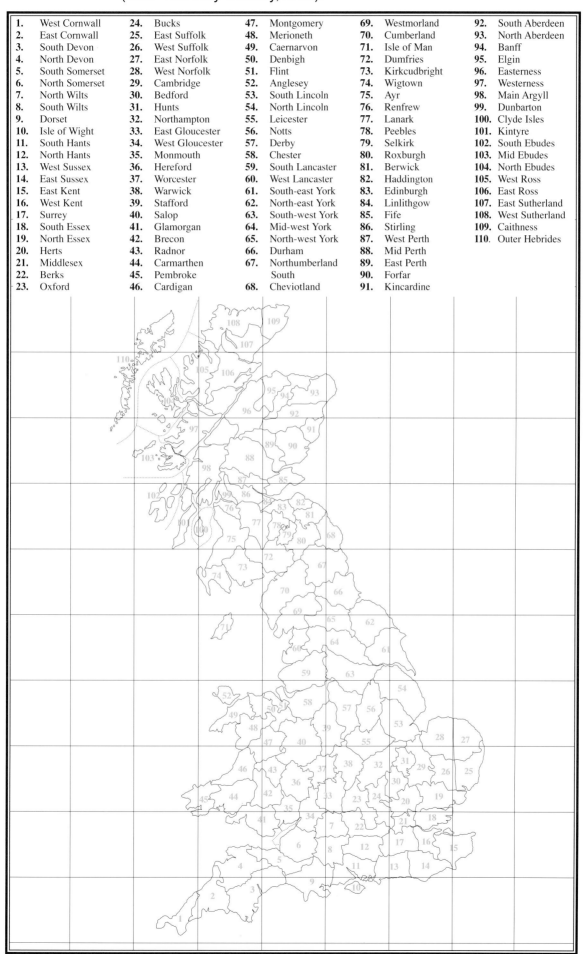

5.2.8 Identification of populations arising from reintroductions

The increasing availability of wild polecats trapped in growing numbers during predator control (Tapper, 1992; Packer & Birks, 1999), and the ease with which they can be bred successfully in captivity (D. Gow, pers. comm.), has ensured a supply of animals for those interested in captive-breeding and re-establishing the species in parts of its former range. In his review of opportunities for reintroducing British mammals, Yalden (1986) considered the polecat to be the best prospect among the three carnivores nearly exterminated in the 19th century, particularly as such action might hasten its spread from an unproductive upland stronghold. He suggested "Sutherland, Speyside, Cornwall, the Lake District and perhaps the Weald" as possible areas for a trial reintroduction. One animal welfare organisation has publicly mooted the reintroduction of polecats in Britain (Panaman, 1992) and this suggestion has been received unfavourably by landowning and fieldsports interests (Moore, 1992; Wigan, 1992). Resistance by minority interests is one of many problems surrounding the reintroduction of carnivores (Yalden, 1993). Probably as a result of such intolerance towards predators, still entrenched in some sectors of the rural community (Tubbs, 1997), polecat reintroductions have tended to be carried out covertly (eg. Jones, 1992a). In addition to the deliberate release of polecats, the growing interest among ferret-keepers in breeding polecat-like stock increases the likelihood that such animals might survive and become established in the wild (see Section 7).

There have been several reports of deliberate reintroductions of polecats, mainly since 1970, in parts of both Scotland and England (eg. Blandford, 1987; Jones, 1992a; Birks, 1993). These have been carried out by people acting in a private capacity rather than as part of any nature conservation organisation. Because of the unofficial and covert nature of these exercises, details of the donor stock, numbers of animals involved and dates and locations of releases are difficult to acquire. However, some information was made available to Jones (1992a), who interviewed a number of individuals involved in polecat releases as part of an unpublished Honours project. During the VWT survey, efforts were made to identify and interview people with information about polecat reintroductions or translocations.

Where established populations of unknown origin (ie. in the absence of any admission of reintroductions, translocations or escapes) were identified at least 30km outside the species' known range, it was assumed that these had probably resulted from reintroductions or translocations.

5.3 Results

5.3.1 The number of records

A total of 1,036 post-1989 polecat records was gathered during this survey, of which 455 (43.9%) related to specimens examined by the VWT staff and their collaborators. Spanning an eight-year period, this compares favourably with the 1,385 records for the species accumulated by the BRC relating to the period 1960-1991 (Arnold, 1993). In the VWT survey, yearly variation in the number of records relating to the period 1990-1997 simply reflects changes in the scale of publicity appealing for records. Figure 5.2 shows that nearly half of all records were derived from 1993 (when the main recording effort was initiated) and 1994.

5.3.2 The type of polecat records received

The type of each record received was known in most cases (97.5%). These are presented in broad categories in Table 5.1 and discussed below.

5.3.2.1 Road casualties

In common with Arnold's (1993) BRC data, road casualties were the most abundant source of polecat records. In the VWT survey two thirds of all records were in this category (see Table 5.1), compared with 37.5% in Arnold's sample. Road casualties dominated the records in every month except January and December (see Figure 5.3a).

The monthly variation in the volume of records shown in Figure 5.3a reflects that detected by Arnold (1993), with a spring peak corresponding with the mating season, and a larger autumn peak corresponding with the dispersal and recruitment of juveniles to the adult population. Where the sex of road casualties could be determined (in 59.1% of cases), males outnumbered females by 2.4:1. Figure 5.3b shows the extent to which the pattern of road casualties differed markedly between the sexes. For six months of the year, between December and May, female road casualties were very scarce, whilst male numbers peaked during the mating season in the same period. Among road casualties, the earliest heavily pregnant female (based on external examination only) was recovered in late April, and the earliest lactating female occurred on 19th May. The rise in female road casualties in June (the

Figure 5.2. Yearly variation in the number of polecat records where year is known, 1990-1997 (*n*=1019).

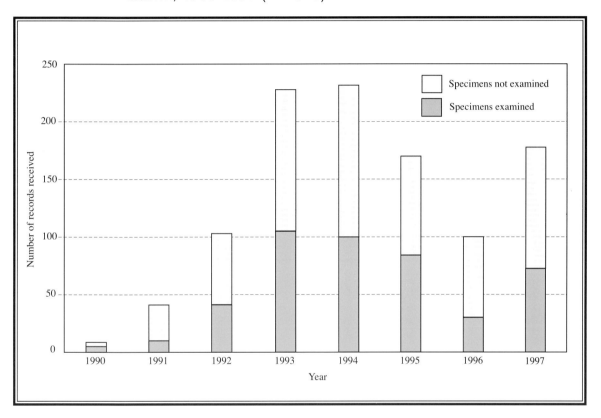

Table 5.1. The relative occurrence of six categories of polecat records, 1990-1997.

Nature of polecat record	Number of records	Percentage of all records
Road casualty	700	67.6
Live sighting	146	14.1
Trapped	140	13.5
Unknown	26	2.5
Dead in farmyard	15	1.4
Miscellaneous	9	0.9

Figure 5.3a. Monthly variation in the number of polecat records received, 1990-1997.

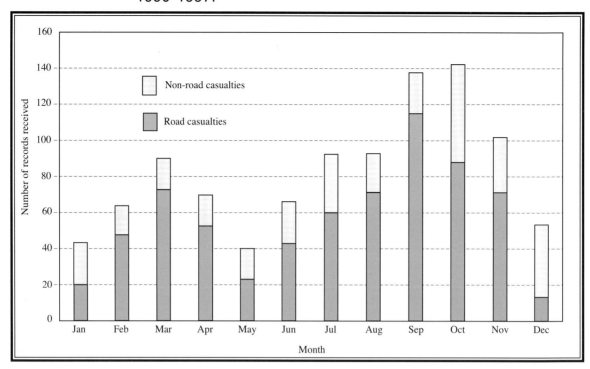

Figure 5.3b. Monthly variation in the number of road casualty polecats of known sex, 1990-1997.

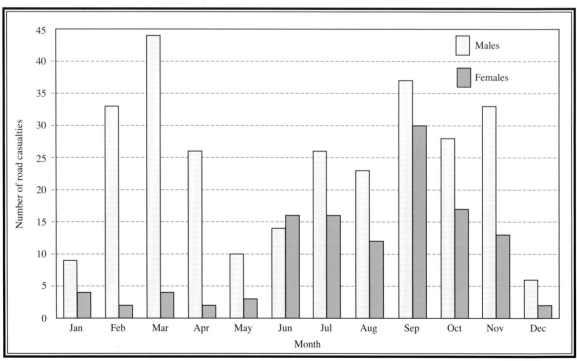

only month in which females outnumbered males) corresponds with the main lactation and early weaning period, when breeding females are especially active. Of 29 road casualty adult females examined between May and July inclusive, 69% showed evidence of lactation. The earliest date on which a juvenile occurred as a road casualty was 3rd June, though a live juvenile was recovered by a road in Gloucestershire on 20th May (presumably following the death of a breeding female). Until August all juvenile records were of apparently dependent animals, often with a number of siblings killed with their mother at the same location. The annual peak in road casualties occurred in September, when dispersing juveniles dominated the records.

36

The importance of road casualties as a source of data on polecats raises questions about the influence that the uneven distribution of roads might exert on the geographical variation in the volume of records. For example, Walton (1968b) suggested that the relative absence of roads on high ground in Wales could explain why he received few records from mountainous areas such as the Brecon Beacons and Snowdonia in the 1960s. This question was examined in the VWT survey by comparing the number of records (of all categories) received, and corpses examined, with the length of main roads in 71 10km squares in three English counties: Shropshire, Herefordshire and Worcestershire (these counties were chosen because they generated the greatest volume and geographical spread of records, and because they include both upland and lowland areas with contrasting 'A' road density).

Mean 'A' class road length per 10km square was 21.197±10.339km. Significant positive correlations were apparent between road length and both the numbers of corpses recovered and the volume of all records received per

Plate 3. *Male polecat road casualty near Malvern, Worcestershire, November 1991. Road casualties comprised 68% of the polecat records received by the VWT during the 1990s.*

square (see Table 5.2). Of these two correlations, the relationship between road length and the number of corpses examined was the stronger, perhaps because a high proportion of the corpses examined were road casualties.

Table 5.2. Correlation statistics illustrating the influence of 'A' road density on the number of polecat records received in 71 10km squares in Shropshire, Herefordshire and Worcestershire, 1990-1997.

Category of records	Mean number per 10km square	Correlation between number of records and road length in 10km squares	Sample size	Probability value
Corpses examined by the VWT	2.324±3.923	$r = 0.570$	$n=71$	$p<0.01$
All polecat records received	5.268±5.135	$r = 0.263$	$n=71$	$p<0.05$

5.3.2.2 Live sightings

Approximately half of all live sightings (51%) of polecats were reported by recorders driving vehicles along roads. Most records (88.2%) included some information about the behaviour of the animals observed. Polecats were commonly seen crossing roads, but many sightings related to other activities such as eating or carrying prey on roads, playing, fighting and mating (see Figure 5.4). In addition, a number of sightings involved animals observed on roadside verges, or moving along (as opposed to across) the centre or sides of roads. Two of these latter sightings concerned animals which ran along the road surface beside or ahead of vehicles for many tens of metres. It is significant that approximately half (48%) of the recorded sightings of polecats on roads (where behaviour was described) were of animals which were not merely crossing roads, but were engaged in other activities, including feeding and carrying prey. Since polecats are reported to forage for carrion along roadsides, this inevitably makes them likely to be killed by vehicles. However, the fact that road-based sightings are concentrated during the hours of darkness (39 out of 44 sightings where the time was specified) might limit the death toll in those months when night-time traffic densities are low.

Away from roads, live sightings of polecats were reported from a range of contexts. Several were seen in or close to areas of human activity or habitation, such as farmyards (3 records), gardens (13) and outbuildings (6). Four records came from people watching or studying badgers at setts (including two who sent videotapes to the VWT of polecats at setts). Three records came from ferreters or ferret-keepers: two reported bolting polecats from rabbit warrens; the third reported a wild male polecat visiting ferret cages during the mating season.

Figure 5.4. The behaviour of live polecats seen on roads (*n*=67), 1990-1997.

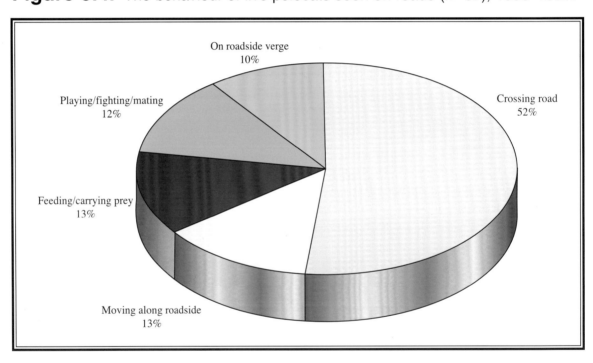

5.3.2.3 Trapped polecats

Records of trapped polecats fell into two broad categories. Those where the animal was known to have been live-trapped and released unharmed (86), and those where one or more animals were killed (54). Records from the VWT's polecat live-trapping scheme (see Section 6 and Birks, 1997) dominated the former sample, though in this case only one record was derived from each of the 66 1km squares in which polecats were caught, regardless of the number of animals involved. Beyond the VWT trapping study, polecat live-captures were recorded in cage traps set for rabbits (7 records), squirrels (2) and rats (2). One of the rabbit trap records related to five polecats caught at one site in Northamptonshire. Since such traps are not normally baited with material attractive to polecats, it is probable that the polecats were attracted into them by the smell of the target prey species. Following completion of this survey, a polecat was trapped in a cage trap set for badgers during a field study in Gloucestershire (L. Rogers, pers. comm.).

Because of the volume of road casualty records received, no particular effort was made to obtain records and corpses of polecats caught and/or killed during predator control operations. However, a few records were collected incidentally from gamekeepers and farmers. These included an animal caught accidentally in a rabbit snare, and animals killed in 'tunnel' traps (19), rat traps (3) and one killed in a spring trap set in a rabbit burrow. Polecats were also deliberately killed after being live-trapped in cage traps set for rabbits (5) and mink (3). A further eight polecats were recorded hanging on gamekeepers' gibbets. With some estates catching as many as 40 polecats a year (Tapper, 1992; Packer & Birks, 1999), the records received from gamekeepers in the VWT survey clearly represent a very small fraction of the available total in this category.

5.3.2.4 Found dead in farmyard

Walton (1970) described the discovery of dead polecats in Welsh farmyards following the use of rodenticides, and suggested that this mortality was evidence of secondary poisoning. Subsequently, Shore et al. (1996) confirmed the extent to which such poisoning occurred in polecats in the English Midlands, and Birks (1998) showed how the species' use of farmyards makes it especially vulnerable to rodenticides. Both these studies cautioned that the true level of polecat mortality due to rodenticides is largely unseen, because most animals probably die out of sight in barns and haystacks on private premises. Nonetheless, the 15 occurrences of polecats found dead in farmyards in this study is perhaps a further indication that this form of mortality is not uncommon.

5.3.2.5 Miscellaneous

Other records included three animals killed by dogs, one killed by rats, one killed by a leopard (in a Wildlife Park), two shot and one killed by a train.

5.3.2.6 Polecats recovered by Wildlife Rescue Centres

In addition to the records listed in Table 5.1, several reports were received of polecats taken in by individuals or establishments specialising in wildlife rescue and rehabilitation. The animals were usually recovered from roadsides after collision with vehicles or as apparently orphaned juveniles. One of these involved a young male recovered soon after a lactating female was killed on a road near Wybunbury in Cheshire in 1997. This animal was housed at the RSPCA's Stapeley Grange Animal Hospital until its release at Wybunbury Moss National Nature Reserve in October 1997 in conjunction with English Nature. A 'soft' release method was used, involving construction of a temporary pen at the release site in which the animal was housed and fed. Feeding inside the pen was maintained for several weeks after the polecat was given access to the outside by locking open the door to the pen.

5.3.3 The geographical distribution of records

Following the convention adopted by earlier authors (see Section 4), in the VWT survey distribution is normally depicted by 10km squares. Figure 5.5a shows the distribution of the 323 squares from which valid records were received by the VWT survey; Figure 5.5b shows the 201 squares (62.2% of the total) from which specimens were recovered for examination. Photographs of a small but geographically widespread sample of these specimens are presented in Plates 3, 4, 5 and 11 in order to illustrate the appearance of the species in a range of forms (fresh road casualties, museum skins and mounted specimens).

Both maps in Figure 5.5 show the concentration of recent records in the English West Midlands, with outlier populations in Argyll in the west of Scotland, the north-west of England, the East Midlands and the south of England (Hampshire and Wiltshire). In the case of these outlier populations, which are known or presumed to have originated from reintroductions or translocations since 1970, 67.1% of the 73 positive squares were determined on the basis of examination of specimens.

Figure 5.5b.

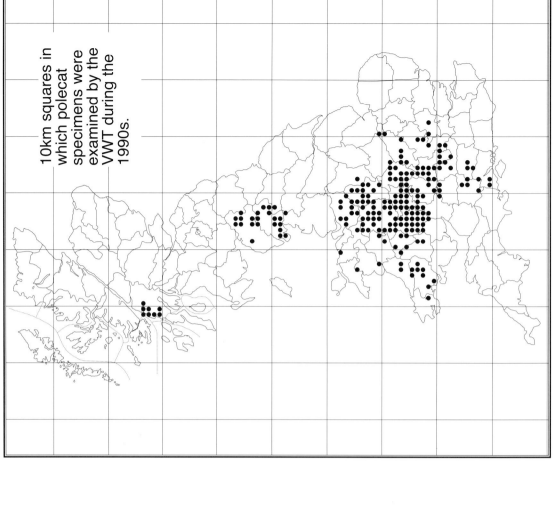

10km squares in which polecat specimens were examined by the VWT during the 1990s.

Figure 5.5a.

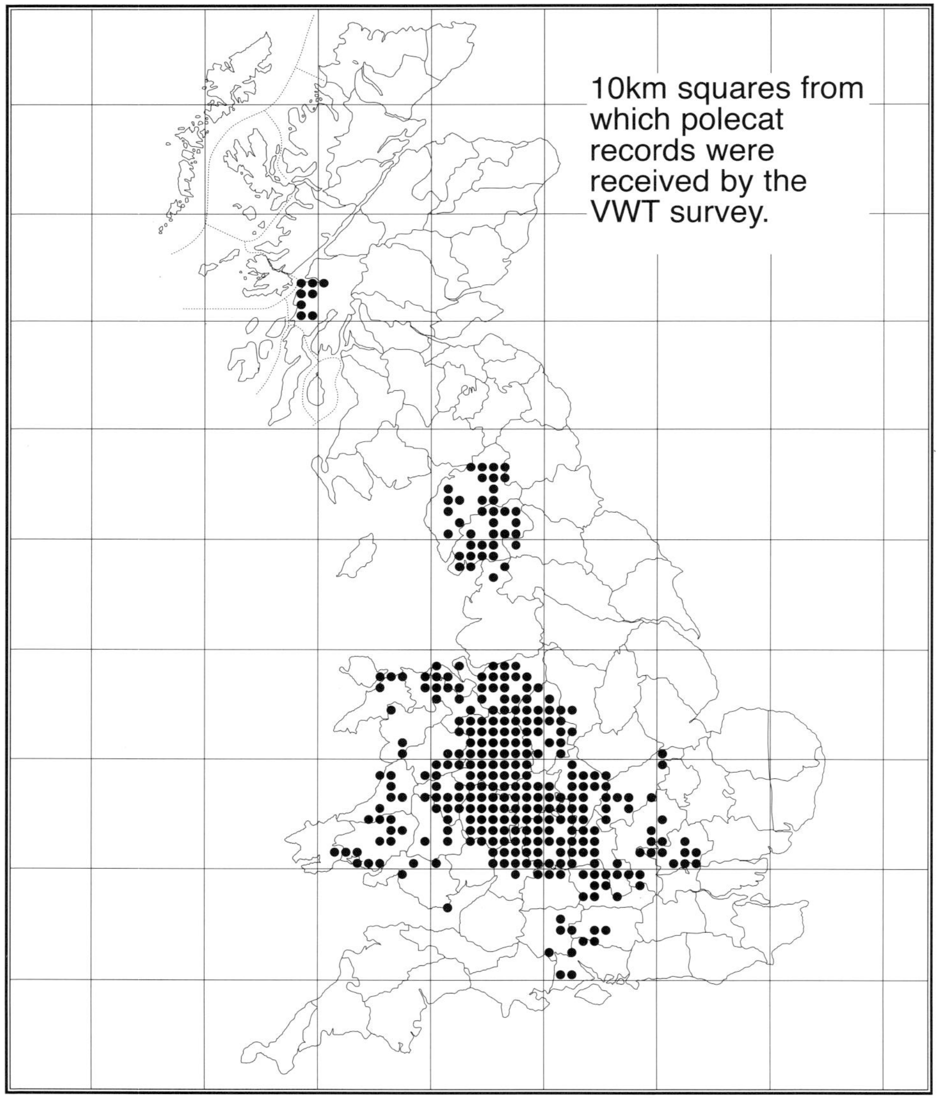

10km squares from which polecat records were received by the VWT survey.

40

Plate 4. *1990s road casualty specimens from the polecat's naturally expanding range in the English Midlands:*

a) John Jones with a male from Alcester, October 1992

b) the first confirmed late 20th-century polecats from Leicestershire - a female (top) from Lutterworth, October 1997, and a male (bottom) from Wibtoft, July 1994 (both in Leicester City Museum)

c) dorsal and

d) ventral views of Staffordshire polecats from the 1990s (in City Museum and Art Gallery, Stoke-on-Trent).

The 228 new 10km squares (ie. squares from which polecats were recorded as absent during previous surveys since 1950) added by the VWT survey are presented in Figure 5.6. This illustrates the scale of the recent eastward expansion from the west of England and shows the addition of 12 new Welsh squares, mainly in the south and north-east of the Principality. Excluding the presumed reintroduced populations, the greatest concentrations of new positive 10km squares were recorded in Cheshire, Staffordshire, Worcestershire, Warwickshire, Gloucestershire and Oxfordshire.

Figure 5.7 combines all new distribution data from the VWT survey with those from previous surveys since 1950, to illustrate the best estimate of the polecat's British range in 1997. Remarkably, given the four decades of recording which have focused mainly on Wales, three 10km squares (SH92, SN89 and SO18) remain blank within, or very close to, the polecat's historical stronghold. In view of the long-standing evidence of well-established populations in adjacent areas, it is inconceivable that the species is truly absent from these squares. The most probable explanation is that they have not generated records because they are located in remote upland areas with very low human populations and low road densities ('A' class roads are absent from all but one square, SO18, which contains a length of less than 5km).

Further south, the absence of records from at least 17 squares in south Wales between Llanelli and Chepstow cannot be explained in the same way. This area includes the south Wales valleys, which support the highest human population and 'A' class road densities in the Principality. The VWT survey made a particular effort to solicit records from this area; Walton (1970) made a similar appeal over 25 years previously, noting that "polecats seem to

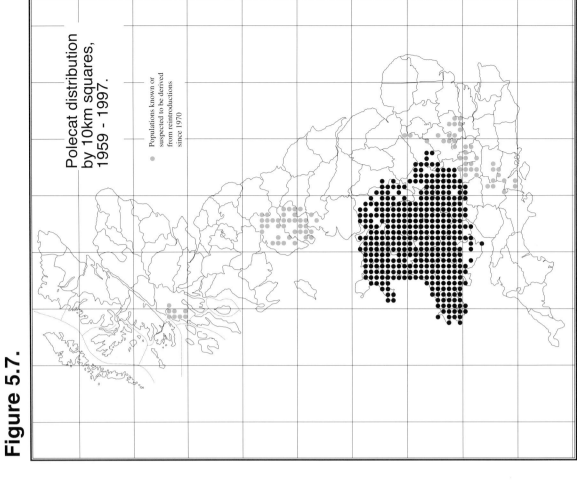

Figure 5.7.

Polecat distribution by 10km squares, 1959 - 1997.

- Populations known or suspected to be derived from reintroductions since 1970

Figure 5.6.

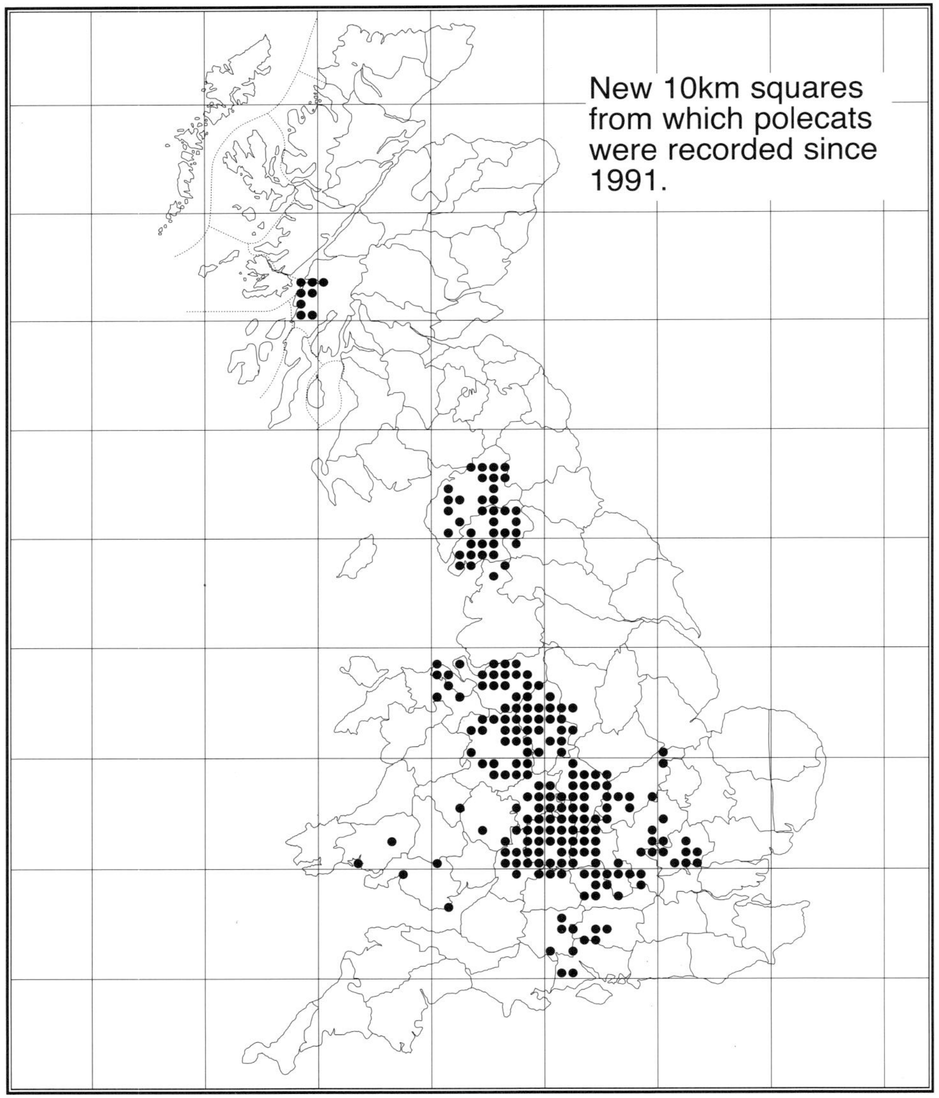

New 10km squares from which polecats were recorded since 1991.

42

be flourishing in the wet coastal area between Cardiff and Newport". Despite this observation, it seems reasonable to conclude that polecats remain absent or very scarce in much of industrial south Wales. Likewise the species remains very scarce on Anglesey, though a series of road casualties recorded since August 1996 adjacent to the two bridges connecting the island to the mainland (K. Walton, pers. comm.) suggest that it is now re-establishing itself.

In England the polecat is now firmly re-established in the West Midlands. In 1997 it had a continuous distribution from the southern fringes of Manchester in the north to the Stroud/Cirencester area in Gloucestershire in the south; from the Welsh border this continuous distribution extended eastward as far as the western edge of the Peak District in Cheshire, Staffordshire and Derbyshire in the north, and to the western parts of Northamptonshire and Oxfordshire in the south (the large conurbation surrounding Birmingham appears as a significant gap in the current range). Records from the outer fringes of the polecat's main range included evidence of reproduction in the form of corpses of either juveniles or lactating females.

Beyond this main English range lie further populations which are believed to have derived from reintroductions (see Figure 5.7 and Section 5.3.5). Most are currently isolated from the naturally-expanding population. However, records from 14 10km squares in south Buckinghamshire, south-east Oxfordshire and north Berkshire (SP40, SP60, SU39, SU49, SU59, SU69, SU79, SU89, SU48, SU58, SU88, SU37, SU47, SU67), which now connect with the south-east of the natural range described above, are believed to derive from reintroductions in the Reading area (see Section 5.3.5.7).

The current status of polecats in all the counties of mainland Britain is summarised briefly in Appendix 1. This table also presents data on extinction rates derived from Langley & Yalden (1977), and suggests probable periods of re-entry into counties where relevant.

5.3.4 A quantitative assessment of range expansion

Table 5.3 and Figure 5.8 illustrate the numerical extent to which the VWT survey has added to the known range of the polecat in Britain. Since Arnold's (1993) 1991 distribution map the number of 10km squares in which the polecat is known to occur has almost doubled (93% increase). Moreover, the addition of 208 10km squares to the known range of the polecat in England alone represents an apparent expansion of over 400% in this country since 1991. The data in Table 5.3 and Figure 5.7 confirm that the polecat now occurs over a wider area in England than it does in Wales.

Table 5.3. Changes in the number of 10km squares recorded as occupied by polecats in Britain, 1959-1997.

Recording unit in which bulk of 10km square lies	Number of 10km squares recorded as positive by previous authors 1959-1991	Number of 10km squares in which polecats were recorded in 1993-1997	Number of new positive 10km squares added during 1993-1997	Cumulative total of 10km squares in which polecats were recorded 1959-1997
Wales	194	62	12	206
England	51	253	208	259
Scotland	0	8	8	8
Total	245	323	228	473

However, it is important to consider what proportions of this range expansion can be attributed to a 'catching up' following a period of conservative recording (see Section 4.6.8), to natural recolonisation, or to the establishment of previously unrecorded populations as a consequence of reintroductions or translocations. Figure 5.8 is derived largely from earlier survey data already presented in Section 4 and gives an indication of the possible influence of conservative recording. The steady accretion of new 10km squares apparent during the 1960s and 1970s is clearly not maintained by the three surveys dated 1983, 1986 and 1991. Data presented in Section 4 suggest that, had the initial 1960s and 1970s recruitment rate of 7.8 new 10km squares per year been maintained subsequently, the polecat's range in 1991 would have covered 319 squares. This would account for 32% of the new squares added to the polecat's range since 1991 by the VWT survey (see Figure 5.9).

In reality, expanding populations tend to follow a sigmoid rather than linear progression as shown by the otter's current recovery in Britain (Strachan & Jefferies, 1996). Instead of envisaging a single recovery curve, there is a case for viewing the polecat's expansion in Wales and England as separate events, or at least as two curves out of phase. The recolonisation of Wales is largely complete and, constrained by the peninsula shape of the Principality, population expansion must be approaching the top of the recovery curve. In contrast, animals spreading from Wales into the relatively limitless expanse of the English Midlands would have started a new recovery curve. This English recovery is still at an early stage, with the rate of expansion likely to be accelerating rather than constant if habitat quality is adequate.

Figure 5.8. Changes in the number of 10km squares recorded as occupied by the polecat in Britain in successive distribution surveys (see Section 4.6 for details of surveys up to 1991).

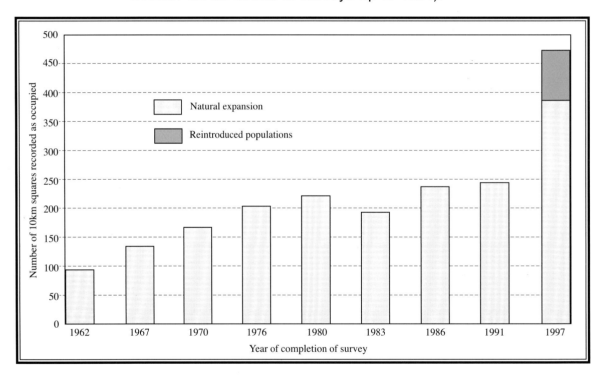

Reintroduced populations in England and Scotland were believed to occupy 87 10km squares in 1997 (see Figure 5.7), and Figure 5.8 indicates the relatively small (18%) contribution that these make to the cumulative total of squares now occupied by the polecat. More significantly, however, Figure 5.9 indicates that these reintroduced populations represent 38% of the new squares added by the VWT survey since Arnold's (1993) distribution map for 1991. Some of these reintroduced populations had clearly existed for some time (see Section 5.3.5), yet previous recording exercises had failed to register their presence. If these assumptions about the contribution of reintroduced populations, and the effects of earlier conservative recording described above, are correct, natural recolonisation constitutes only 30% of the apparent range increase since 1991.

Figure 5.9. Estimated contributions of three main causes of the apparent range expansion of the polecat since 1991.

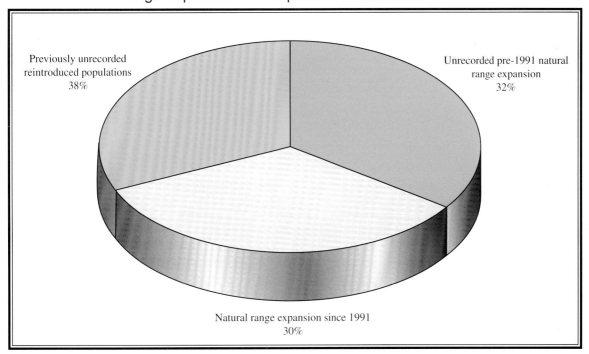

Previously unrecorded
reintroduced populations
38%

Unrecorded pre-1991 natural
range expansion
32%

Natural range expansion since 1991
30%

5.3.5 Populations arising from reintroductions

The 87 10km squares believed to be occupied by polecats as a consequence of reintroductions or escapes from captivity are shown in Figure 5.7. Where it has been possible to ascertain details, it is thought that these reintroductions have mostly involved pure polecat stock of Welsh origin, rather than ferret hybrids. These populations are located in three main areas. They occur in the Scottish Highlands, in the north-west of England and in a discontinuous band running from the East Midlands to central southern England. The origins of these populations, as far as they are known, are considered below.

5.3.5.1 Argyll, Scotland

An unidentified source informed Jones (1992a) of the release of about 60 polecats from 1970 onwards near Loch Sween, Argyll; others were released on the northern shore of Loch Fyne between Lochgilphead and Inverary. Another source told of the release of 15-20 pregnant female and about five male polecats at Ardfern on Loch Craignish, Argyll. These Argyll releases would appear to have been successful, since apparently true polecats are now re-established over a minimum area of eight 10km squares and are increasingly recovered as road casualties (Craik & Brown, 1997).

5.3.5.2 Loch Ness, Scotland

A further release was reported to Jones (1992a) near the village of Dores on Loch Ness in 1982. This involved fewer animals (no more then ten), and the source of this information doubts whether the exercise has been successful due in part to persecution by gamekeepers.

5.3.5.3 Central Highlands, Scotland

The VWT has been told of the release of polecats, starting in the early 1990s, at sites in the central Highlands of Scotland. There is currently insufficient evidence to be certain whether this exercise has resulted in successful re-establishment of a self-sustaining population. However, polecat-like specimens have been recovered recently from near Crieff (Craik & Brown, 1997). In August 1998 two apparently pure polecat road casualties were reported on the A9 road between Pitlochry and Dunkeld.

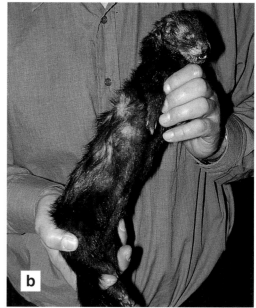

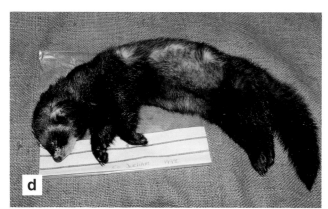

Plate 5. *1990s specimens from polecat populations believed to be derived from post-1970 reintroductions:*

a) *road casualty female from near Aylesbury, Buckinghamshire, August 1990 (specimen in Aylesbury Museum)*

b) *road casualty male from near Haynes, Bedfordshire, November 1996 (specimen in Bedford Museum)*

c) *road casualty female (lactating) from Martin Down, Hampshire, June 1997*

d) *male killed near Staindrop, County Durham, November 1998.*

5.3.5.4 Elsewhere in Scotland

Reports of polecat-like specimens have been received from Speyside and near Helmsdale in Caithness. Several Scottish islands support populations of feral ferrets which are commonly called 'polecats' by local inhabitants (see Section 7).

5.3.5.5 Northern England

Jones (1992a) reported an unsuccessful release of 'polecat-ferret hybrids' into Grizedale Forest, south Cumbria during the mid-1960s. Since 1978, however, a more sustained programme involving at least 150 animals released over 15 years at several sites in Cumbria has clearly been successful. Having interviewed one of the individuals involved, Jones (1992a) established that, initially at least, the animals released were not fully pure polecats. From the early 1980s onwards, however, pure polecats of Welsh origin were reportedly obtained for release, or for captive breeding to generate stock for release. As a result of this exercise the polecat is now widely re-established in Cumbria, and has begun to recolonise the adjacent counties of Northumberland, Lancashire and possibly Durham (see Plate 5d). This population now occupies a minimum area of 38 10km squares.

5.3.5.6 Hertfordshire/Bedfordshire, England

The VWT has been told of the release of a total of approximately 40 polecats at several sites in Hertfordshire. Most releases took place in 1982, with two further releases, each of six animals, in 1995 and 1996. Subsequent records confirm that this exercise has led

46

to the re-establishment of polecats in parts of western and central Hertfordshire. Polecats have also been recorded since 1990 from adjacent parts of the neighbouring county of Buckinghamshire, and since 1994 from adjacent parts of the neighbouring county of Bedfordshire (Tack, 1995 and see Plate 5b), suggesting that the Hertfordshire population has expanded northwards and westwards. By the end of 1997 these East Midlands polecats had been recorded from 13 10km squares.

5.3.5.7 South Buckinghamshire/ south-east Oxfordshire/north Berkshire, England

The origin of polecats in this area is difficult to establish with certainty, not least because the population is now contiguous with the naturally expanding range of the species. Confirmed evidence of polecats in the southern Chilterns between Princes Risborough and Goring dates from 1995, and near Aylesbury from 1990 (see Plate 5a). However, unconfirmed (no corpses available) 1980s records have been received from a reliable observer in the Henley-on-Thames area (V. Lewis, pers. comm.). At that time the area concerned lay some 40+ km to the east of the polecat's main advancing front in the far west of Oxfordshire, and thus the records cannot readily be explained in terms of the species' natural range expansion. It is conceivable that this population arose as a result of a reported (but unconfirmed) release of polecats 'near Reading'. Since the mid-1990s this population has apparently expanded westward into the vice-county of Berks to connect with the eastern fringe of the polecat's naturally expanding range. The Chilterns' population is apparently so well-established that on a sporting estate in south Buckinghamshire one gamekeeper claimed to have killed 20 polecats in the spring of 1996 (Dr. A. George, pers. comm.). There is ample evidence of reproduction in this population in the form of corpses of lactating females and juveniles, and photographs of a mother and young.

5.3.5.8 Hampshire/Wiltshire, England

Since 1994 polecats have been recovered as road casualties from parts of Hampshire (Jordan, 1997) and Wiltshire. Discrete 'pockets' appear to be established in the Micheldever area (M. Jordan, pers. comm.) and on the fringes of the New Forest. The origin of these is unknown, but their distance from the advancing front suggests that they are most unlikely to represent part of the natural range expansion of the species. Both these nuclei predate the alleged release in 1996 of a small number of animals in the New Forest. By the end of 1997 the species had been recorded from 12 10km squares in Hampshire and Wiltshire, and unconfirmed reports had also been received from the adjacent county of Dorset. The corpses examined from Hampshire included at least one lactating female (see Plate 5c). These populations are the only ones known to be established south of the M4 Motorway corridor.

5.3.5.9 Elsewhere in England

Reports of further polecat releases since 1980 (albeit largely unconfirmed) have been received from Cornwall, Kent and near Thetford in East Anglia. There is also very recent, unconfirmed evidence of a nucleus established in north Somerset to the south-west of Bristol. There is every possibility that further unrecorded reintroductions of polecats have occurred in the recent past, either within the polecat's current range (in which case it is impossible to estimate their contribution to the current situation), or elsewhere.

5.3.6 Geographical variation in the abundance of records

As explained in Section 5.2.3, it was not possible fully to standardise recording effort geographically in this survey because of the many variables believed to influence the generation of polecat records. Nevertheless, the very widespread publicity led to such marked geographical variations in the volume of records received (see Table 5.4) that the patterns observed must have some biological significance. If this assumption is reasonable, then Table 5.4 suggests that the polecat is considerably more abundant in the western vice-counties of Salop, Hereford and Worcester than in those areas more distant from the species' historical Welsh stronghold.

Table 5.4. Variation in the number and sex ratio of polecat records received from English vice-counties, 1990-1997.

Vice-county	Number of polecat records 1990-1997	Number of polecat specimens examined 1990-1997	Road casualty sex ratio (males : females)
Berks	10	5	2 : 1
Oxford	55	28	5 : 1
Bucks	12	8	1 : 1
Cambridge	2	2	1 : 0
Bedford	8	4	1 : 1
Northampton	19	9	4 : 1
East Gloucester	40	13	1.25 : 1
West Gloucester	14	7	6 : 0
Hereford	176	92	2.4 : 1
Worcester	107	49	2.2 : 1
Warwick	80	44	1.7 : 1
Stafford	75	47	2.3 : 1
Salop	132	39	2.6 : 1
Leicester	2	2	1 : 1
Derby	9	2	3 : 0
Chester	68	17	2.5 : 1
West Lancaster	2	1	1 : 0
Westmorland	69	19	1.86 : 1
Cumberland	24	14	0.6 : 1
Northumberland South	1	1	1 : 0
Herts	11	1	2 : 1
South Hants	3	2	3 : 0
North Hants	11	6	8 : 1
North Wilts	2	2	2 : 0
South Wilts	4	4	1 : 0

Notably, the vice-county of Westmorland (corresponding approximately with the southern part of the modern county of Cumbria) generated a similar volume of records to the Midland vice-counties of Chester, Stafford, Warwick, East Gloucester and Oxford. Polecats are increasingly well-established in these counties and Table 5.4 suggests that the reintroduced Cumbrian polecat population has achieved a comparable status at least in the southern part of its range.

5.3.7 The estimated pattern of recovery

In the absence of either constant historical recording effort or systematic monitoring, it is impossible to reconstruct the polecat's pattern of recovery with complete accuracy. However, the data collected by this and previous mapping exercises (summarised in Section 4.6) can be used to estimate the pattern of range expansion through the past four decades. The estimated limits of the changing distribution for the middle of each decade are shown in Figure 5.10. This shows the position of successive southward (in Wales) and eastward-moving 'fronts' between the mid-1960s and mid-1990s. Initially, between the mid-1960s and mid-1970s, eastward expansion was apparently very limited. Subsequently, however, the front in England has advanced eastward at mean rates of 3.5km per year between the mid-1970s and mid-1980s, and 4.3km between the mid-1980s and mid-1990s. Remarkably, these figures compare closely with Strachan and Jefferies' (1996) estimated rate of range expansion by the otter in England of 3.6km per year. The apparent increase in the rate of the polecat's range expansion might be a consequence of higher reproductive success in the more productive lowland habitats encountered east of the Welsh border.

Figure 5.10. An estimate of the changing limits to the polecat's main British range during the 20th century. Outlying or reintroduced populations are not shown. The green area shows the main 1915 range estimated by Langley and Yalden (1977). Subsequent range limits are:
a) mid-1960s, based on Walton (1968b);
b) mid-1970s, based on Arnold (1978);
c) mid-1980s, based on Blandford (1987), Tapper (1992) and data from the current survey;
d) mid-1990s, based on the current survey.

The curves have been smoothed by, for example, excluding isolated points.

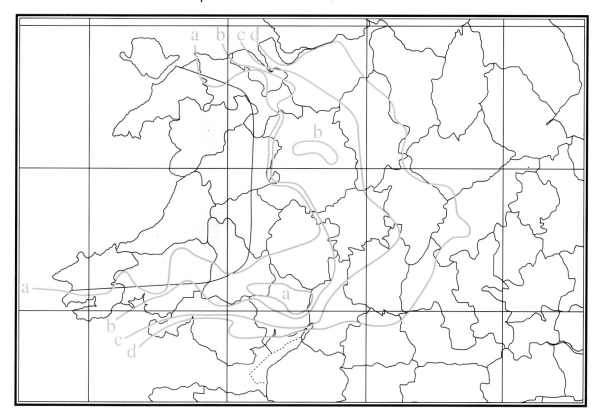

The more advanced eastward front in the southern half of the polecat's range is apparent in all time periods, suggesting that the presence of the species in north Herefordshire and south Shropshire in the early 1960s represented a significant 'head start'.

In addition to this historical effect, the eastward spread in the northern half of the polecat's range might be expected (in future) to proceed more slowly because of the less favourable, upland habitat (the Peak District) dominating north-east Cheshire, north-east Staffordshire and northern Derbyshire. In contrast, the range to the south is dominated by fertile lowland farmland.

Whilst the northern limits to the polecat's naturally expanding range in England are currently defined by inhospitable habitat in the Manchester conurbation, there are no such constraints further south. It is surprising that the apparently vigorous eastward expansion has not been matched by a similar move southward. For example, the polecat was described as returning to Gloucestershire in the period 1950-1964 by Langley and Yalden (1977); this was based upon Walton (1964) recording it at one location in the north-west of the county (and at several sites in adjacent Monmouthshire) in 1959-62. However, 35 years later the species has yet to spread more than 30km towards the south of the county. This compares with mean eastward expansion rates of up to 43km per decade shown in Figure 5.10. It is unlikely that the River Severn and M5 Motorway represented such barriers that southward expansion was significantly delayed, since there is no evidence that the same two barriers hindered eastward expansion further north in the polecat's range. Currently the M4 Motorway lies just beyond the southern edge of the polecat's range in Gloucestershire and Wiltshire, so this potential barrier cannot explain the relatively slow rate of recent southward spread.

5.4 Discussion

The VWT survey has confirmed that the polecat's recovery in Britain has continued further into the 1990s, to the extent that the species now occupies a greater land area in England than in its Welsh stronghold. This may come as a surprise to those who view the polecat as primarily a Welsh species. The polecat's recent recovery has much in common with that of two birds of prey, the buzzard and the red kite. Following heavy persecution, all survived in early 20th-century western strongholds - the red kite's being similar in geographical extent to, albeit more southerly than, the polecat's - (Lovegrove, 1990; Tapper, 1992). Subsequently, all have extended their ranges, with reintroductions making a significant contribution in the case of both the red kite (Cross & Davis, 1998) and polecat.

5.4.1 The pattern and causes of polecat recovery

Assumptions that the polecat's current distribution has arisen mainly as a result of a very recent, rapid, natural spread are clearly false. Best estimates from the VWT survey suggest a relatively modest rate of expansion since the mid-1970s, with evidence of an increase since the mid-1980s. The revelation that previous conservative recording and reintroductions or translocations explain most of the apparent recent range expansion has also been made in connection with the Reeves' muntjac, another species which is currently expanding its range in Britain. Chapman *et al.* (1994) recorded a 79% increase in muntjac range in the two years between the preceding survey (Arnold, 1993) and their own in 1993. They demonstrated that the actual rate of muntjac spread, of about 1km per year, is much less impressive than previously assumed. Likewise, the polecat's natural rate of spread since the mid-1980s, estimated at approximately 4km per year, is clearly less dramatic than that suggested by the near-doubling of its recorded British range since 1991.

With the benefit of hindsight, it is clear that the tendency to reject possible polecat records reported some distance from Wales as probable ferrets or hybrids, has contributed to the conservative nature of earlier recording efforts. For example, whilst the recent presence of polecats in Warwickshire was not confirmed until 1992, it is believed that the species may have begun to recolonise the county as early as the 1970s, yet at the time all records were dismissed as improbable (P. Copson, pers. comm.). Similarly, in Northamptonshire, polecats were first confirmed in 1994, yet probably genuine records from the 1980s were rejected at the time (P. Richardson, pers. comm.).

The VWT survey has confirmed the contribution of recent translocations or reintroductions of polecats to the recent expansion. The resulting populations are now greater in extent than the estimated area of natural range expansion since 1991. More significantly, reintroductions have successfully restored the species to parts of its natural British range several decades before these would have been recolonised by natural means. In central southern England, at least one of the populations suspected to have arisen from reintroductions is now beginning to merge with the species' naturally expanding range. However, the covert nature of polecat reintroductions has created some difficulties for the VWT survey. With two or three notable exceptions, information on the dates and locations of releases, and the numbers and sources of stock involved, have been impossible to acquire; as a result, the origins of some of these populations remain uncertain.

The VWT survey's focus upon polecat road casualties proved valuable in many respects. It assisted in achieving the important aim of maximising the number of records supported by unequivocal evidence. It also generated an important collection of specimens which facilitated other areas of research (see Sections 7 and 8.3.11). As an added bonus, it raised awareness of the polecat and its recovery through the involvement of very many people in the collection of road casualties.

The principal factor driving the polecat's natural recovery is believed to be the reduction in persecution early in the 20th century (Langley & Yalden, 1977). Whilst this is generally linked to the decline in gamekeeping since the First World War, Walton (1970) stressed the continued suppressant effect on polecat numbers which commercial rabbit-trapping must have had before myxomatosis destroyed this industry in the 1950s. Tens of thousands of non-selective 'gin traps' were used by professional rabbit trappers who, in order to prevent damage to trapped rabbits which might have affected their market value, tended first to trap out local predators. Since Walton (1970) described Pembrokeshire, Carmarthenshire and south Cardiganshire as amongst the most important areas in Britain for this trade, it is very likely that rabbit trapping hindered the expansion of the polecat's Welsh range in these areas, and probably elsewhere, until the mid-1950s. Blandford (1987) believed that this 1950s' cessation of gin-trapping represented the vital new factor in the polecat's ecology which explained its resurgence thereafter.

An alternative explanation for the post-1950s' increase in polecat numbers is suggested by Jefferies (1992). He argues that the crash in otter populations in 1957-58 (Chanin & Jefferies, 1978), leading to significantly reduced intra-guild predation or interference, was a more likely stimulus to polecat recovery than was the cessation of widespread gin-trapping. Certainly, there is evidence for such intra-guild effects of otters upon mink populations in Britain (Birks, 1990; Strachan & Jefferies, 1996). However, the weak association between polecat activity and wetland habitats in Britain (see Section 8) would suggest a much more limited interaction between this species and the otter. Also, if the otter represented a significant negative pressure, one would expect to have observed a faltering in the polecat's recolonisation where otter populations have recovered. There is no evidence of such an effect.

Although myxomatosis indirectly relieved pressure upon polecat populations, it also removed an important source of prey. Some predators were undoubtedly affected adversely by the sudden reduction in rabbit numbers (Sumption & Flowerdew, 1985). However, there is little evidence of any negative impact upon the polecat's status, perhaps because of the balancing effect of the simultaneous release from trapping pressure. Condry (1991) goes further, noting that "Paradoxically the polecat, which probably relied on rabbits more than any other four-footed predator, increased greatly after myxomatosis, the conclusion being that it gained far more from the departure of the gin trap than it lost by the disappearance of the rabbit". The polecat is still a notable rabbit predator in Britain (see Section 8), so it is not unlikely that the post-myxomatosis recovery in rabbit numbers has positively influenced the pattern of polecat range expansion.

Figure 5.11. National Game Census data showing trends in rabbit and polecat numbers in the west of Britain, 1961-1995.

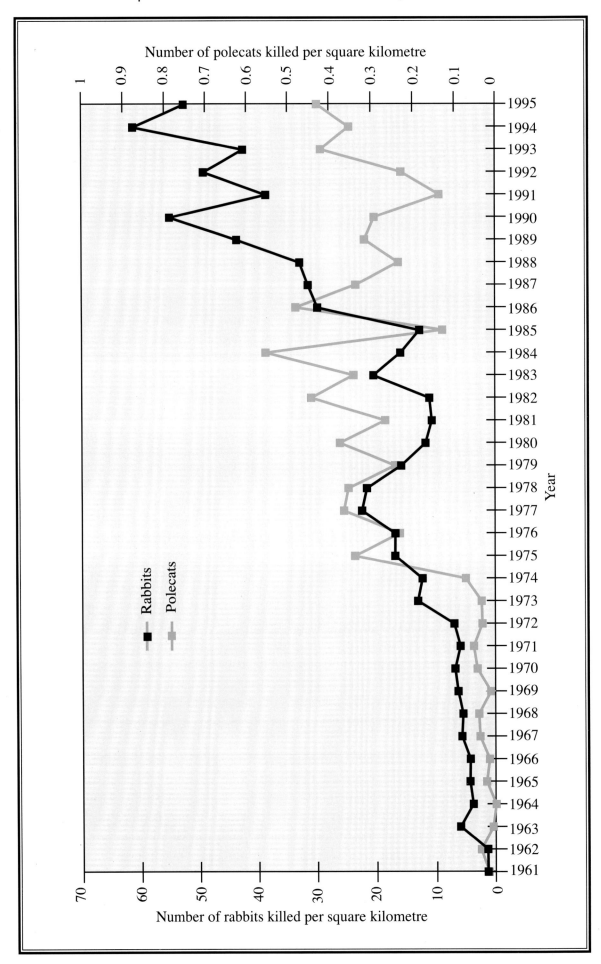

Game Bag data suggest that rabbit numbers remained suppressed in the west of England and Wales until 1973 when a sustained increase began (Trout *et al.*, 1986; and see Figure 5.11). This coincides with the greater estimated rate of polecat range expansion from the mid-1970s onwards. Changes in the numbers of polecats killed by gamekeepers in Wales and the English West Midlands suggest that the population remained suppressed at least until 1974, when a fluctuating increase followed the growth in rabbit numbers before apparently levelling off in the late 1980s (Tapper, 1992; and see Figure 5.11). These sets of Game Bag data on rabbits and polecats are strongly correlated ($r=0.586$, $n=35$, $p<0.001$). The pattern they reveal supports an hypothesis of increasing polecat numbers, fuelled largely by the recovery of rabbit populations in the 1970s.

McDonald and Harris (in press) have shown that recent data on the number of predators trapped by gamekeepers in Britain need to be interpreted carefully in view of changes in trapping effort. They demonstrate that declines in stoats and weasels trapped in Britain are consistent with reduced trapping effort in recent decades, so cannot be relied upon as evidence of population declines. Thus, data from the same source indicating an increase in numbers of polecats trapped may be evidence of an even more significant recovery than that suggested by Figure 5.11. In particular, the levelling off in the number of polecats killed from the late 1980s onwards, shown in Figure 5.11, is likely to be an artefact of reduced trapping effort which masks the real and continuing increase in polecat numbers apparent from other sources.

5.4.2 Prospects for future spread

Data from this distribution survey, from live-trapping studies described in Section 6, and from independent Game Bag records (Tapper, 1992), all indicate that polecat population densities vary geographically, tending to be highest within or close to the species' historical stronghold. Birks (1997) has suggested that a predictable density gradient may exist between the historical source and the perimeter of the polecat's expanding population; he also cautioned that other factors, such as heavy road casualty mortality, may contribute to this picture by depressing polecat numbers in some areas. For example, the VWT survey revealed that areas within the polecat's range with the highest human populations and road densities, such as the south Wales valleys and the English West Midlands conurbation, stand out as incompletely recolonised. Notably, live-trapping data indicate that polecat populations are more patchy towards the fringes of the species' range, and that negative correlations exist between trapping data and the density of major roads (see Section 6.4.3). In Britain traffic densities are highest in the south-east of England (DETR, 1997 and unpublished data) beyond the current limits of the polecat's expanding range. Given the species' vulnerability to traffic, any road casualty effect may, thus, serve to slow its future spread or even to hinder the establishment or maintenance of populations. A similar effect has been described in badger populations in Essex, where road casualty mortality was believed to explain the reduced density of setts near busy roads (Skinner *et al.*, 1991).

There are other reasons to temper assumptions of an unimpeded future spread by the polecat in Britain. Notably, the reported population declines due to agricultural intensification in other parts of Europe indicate the scale of effects that may already be influencing the species in Britain. Here agricultural intensification has caused major deleterious changes to the natural environment since the 1950s, with the result that many wildlife species have shown substantial population declines (Anon., 1984, 1993). Due largely to geographical constraints upon land use, the polecat's hilly, western stronghold has been affected less by agricultural intensification than have the lowlands further east, where the extent of semi-natural habitat is now much more limited (Anon., 1989). Thus, the polecat's current eastward spread is leading it into landscapes which might be regarded as progressively less favourable. Conversely, rabbit populations tend to be higher in the east of Britain than in the west (Trout *et al.*, 1986; Tapper, 1992), so the greater availability of a favoured prey species may counter some of these adverse effects. Whilst there is no reason to believe that the current expansion will not continue (particularly if rabbit numbers remain high), experience from continental Europe suggests that habitat factors might limit polecat population densities in some areas.

Blandford (1987) suggested that the polecat's eastward advance might be slowed by persecution associated with game rearing. There is no evidence from the VWT survey to support this view, despite the fact that sporting estates have been killing polecats in increasing numbers in Wales and the English West Midlands (Tapper, 1992). However, geographical variations in the pattern of persecution mean that the possibility of some effect in future cannot be ruled out. For example, Packer and Birks (1999) have shown that persecution pressure tends to increase towards the fringes of the polecat's range, and Tapper's (1992) data show that gamekeeper numbers are highest beyond the current main range in south-east England. A further consideration is the greater emphasis on widespread tunnel-trapping of ground predators on wild game shoots, which tend to be concentrated in the far east of England (Tapper, 1992).

Recognising that accidental tunnel-trapping of polecats is both common and of doubtful legality, Packer and Birks (1999) have suggested that steps be taken to exclude such non-target animals (a legal requirement, depending upon one's interpretation of the legislation - see Section 4.4) by modifying the design of traps. The Game Conservancy Trust (GCT) has recently designed and tested a device to achieve this end (J. Reynolds, pers. comm.). The widespread adoption of such an exclusion device would aid the conservation of polecats and other species such as pine martens. It would also signal a willingness to adopt more acceptable methods of controlling mammalian predators (Reynolds & Tapper, 1996). Current trap-based control of mammal pests in Britain, which depends heavily upon non-specific, lethal spring traps, conflicts with the trend towards highly specific traps within the EU (M. Swan, pers. comm.). Other pest control practices, such as rodenticide use and rabbit gassing, are also believed to impact more heavily upon polecats towards the fringes of the species' range (Birks, 1998; Packer & Birks, 1999; Shore *et al.*, in press 1999).

5.5 Acknowledgements

We thank all the people, too numerous to name, who contributed to this work by collecting records and corpses of polecats. We are especially indebted to those who, whether professionally or otherwise, fulfilled a co-ordinating role on a county or regional basis. We are, therefore, pleased to thank Clive Craik (Scottish Highlands), Brian Burnett (Flintshire), John Martin, John Webster, Norman Clarke and Steve Hewitt (Cumbria), Jackie Begg and Becky Palmer (Cheshire), David Heaver and Tom Wall (Shropshire), Geoff Halfpenny and Keith Bloor (Staffordshire), Nick Moyes (Derbyshire), Michael Clark (Hertfordshire), Jan Dawson (Leicestershire), Phil Richardson (Northamptonshire), Cliff Tack, Rosemary Brind and Chris Andrew (Bedfordshire), Richard Eckton (Cambridgeshire), Sue Holland and Felicity Burge (Herefordshire), Pam Copson and Jane O'Dell (Warwickshire), Colin Fountain, Vaughan Lewis, Graham Scholey, Adam Grogan and John Campbell (Oxfordshire), Ched George (Buckinghamshire), Rob Macklin, Ros Willder and Mervyn Greening (Gloucestershire), Sally Scott-White (Wiltshire), Mike Averill, Russell Coope and Brian Draper (Worcestershire), Mike and Debbie Jordan, Tim Sykes and staff of the GCT (Hampshire), and Ken Walton and Jean Matthews (Anglesey).

We are very grateful to all those who helped to publicise the appeal for records, especially the County Museums, The National Trust and County Wildlife Trusts. We are grateful to the GCT for access to Game Bag data on polecats and rabbits.

6. DEVELOPMENT OF A METHOD FOR MONITORING POLECATS

J.D.S. Birks, P. Hanson, D.L. Jermyn, H.W. Schofield and K.C. Walton

6.1 Introduction

Monitoring is an important tool in wildlife management and conservation. Unlike simple mapping or recording of distribution and abundance, monitoring involves repeating recording operations at intervals, in ways that allow changes in distribution and abundance to be assessed reliably. Accurate monitoring is essential if the UK Government is to meet its obligations, under the EC Habitats and Species Directive, to maintain or restore the favourable conservation status of key species. Monitoring is especially important in informing decisions about species which are undergoing significant range expansion or contraction, or increasing or declining in numbers within a stable range. The rationale and science behind modern mammal monitoring in Britain are explored thoroughly in '*Proposals for future monitoring of British mammals*', published by the DETR (Macdonald *et al.*, 1998). The authors recommend mammal monitoring based upon well-defined protocols. Precise and detailed definition of the methods of collecting information on distribution and abundance ensures repeatability, and generates robust, quantitative data. The series of national otter surveys conducted at seven-year intervals in Britain since the 1970s (eg. Strachan & Jefferies, 1996) is a good example of this approach.

For the reasons explained in Section 5.2.2, neither sightings nor field signs can be reliably used as the basis for recording polecats. Whilst road casualties may be used for distribution-mapping, several uncontrollable or unquantifiable factors influence the probability of records reaching a recording organisation (Clarke *et al.*, 1998). For example, the behaviour of the species, the density of the road network and the volume of traffic are all likely to influence the occurrence of road casualties, the duration for which they remain identifiable, and the probability that they will be seen and reported. Furthermore, the nature, distribution and timing of publicity appealing for records, and the number and distribution of key individuals and institutions assisting with the survey, are bound to influence the flow of records, as are the abundance and movement patterns of people likely to see and report a road casualty polecat. The shortcomings of this approach are demonstrated by the three blank 10km squares in the polecat's historical stronghold in upland mid-Wales (see Figure 5.7). It is most unlikely that polecats are genuinely absent from these squares; yet none has been recorded from them since organised distribution-mapping began in the 1950s (see Section 5.3.3).

The need to establish some quantitative means of monitoring the changing status of the polecat in Britain, beyond the basic distribution-mapping described in Sections 4 and 5, led the VWT to examine a new approach. This section explains the development and testing of a live-trapping method, involving volunteers, which might form the basis of a national approach to monitoring the species. The main aim was to establish a repeatable system that would generate reliable data on how polecat numbers vary in time and space. A subsidiary aim was to gather data on factors that might affect the numbers of polecats, such as land use, the availability of prey and the density of main roads.

6.2 Methods

Walton (1970) described the polecat as "a very easy animal to trap", noting that gamekeepers had no difficulty in trapping them in gin and spring traps, and that a great many were caught accidentally, mostly in cage traps, during mink control operations in south-west Wales during the 1960s. The VWT distribution survey (see Section 5.3.2.3) includes records of polecats caught accidentally in cage traps set for mink, badgers, rabbits, rats and grey squirrels. The ease with which polecats can be caught in cage traps suggested that live-trapping could be used for monitoring. However, in order to serve this purpose, any live-trapping system needs to be manageable, repeatable (in time and space) and should generate quantitative data reflecting variations in the abundance of polecats. The system developed has been described briefly in Birks (1997). A fuller account is given below.

6.2.1 Choosing a repeatable sampling system

The establishment of a manageable live-trapping system involves decisions about the density of traps, the location, size and shape of sampling points, and the timing and duration of sampling periods. Inevitably these decisions must take account of the population density, activity and spacing behaviour of the species concerned, and the resources available to undertake the work (Macdonald *et al.*, 1998). Where compromises are involved, it is important to consider the limitations that these might impose upon the quality and reliability of data generated. This point was considered by reference to information on polecat movements generated by the VWT radio-tracking study described in Section 8, where there is further discussion of this topic (see Section 8.3.3).

6.2.1.1 Size of trapping unit and density of traps

Trapping and radio-tracking data from the VWT study revealed home range sizes of between 16 and 500ha, and estimated population densities of 0.5-1 individuals per km^2. Blandford's (1986) data from mid-Wales suggest that these figures may be representative of other areas within the species' range, and Harris *et al.* (1995) estimate that British population densities ranged between 0.15-1.5 animals per km^2. Given such a range, a minimum sampling unit of 7km^2, with a minimum trap density of one trap per 15ha, would be necessary to guarantee the opportunity of encountering all individuals present at both extremes. This would have involved 40-50 traps and a daily trap round of tens of kilometres taking several hours to complete. This was clearly impracticable, particularly if volunteers were to be involved. Fortunately, monitoring systems do not have to encounter all individuals in a sampling unit. Sampling a proportion of the individuals present is satisfactory provided it truly reflects variations in abundance.

The 1km grid (composed of what is hereafter referred to as 1km squares) of the United Kingdom's Ordnance Survey (OS) map offers a convenient sampling unit. Every OS map has the 1km squares printed over its other information. However, there might be constraints associated with using a sampling unit comparable to, or smaller than, the size of many individual home ranges. For example, even in areas where polecats are common, only a few individuals might be encountered in a 1km square. At low population densities there is a risk that any individuals present might be missed altogether.

The radio-tracking data presented in Section 8 were used to determine whether the 1km square grid would be an adequate sampling unit (see Section 8.3.3). It was found that radio-tagged polecats occupied only a single main 1km square in one third of tracking sessions (main 1km squares exclude those peripheral squares visited only occasionally by radio-tagged animals); and no more than three 1km squares were visited in over two-thirds of tracking sessions (see Figure 6.1). Thus, in areas of moderate population density, sampling based upon 1km squares of the OS grid was likely to encounter a significant proportion of the polecats present. To improve the chances of encountering polecats, the density of traps was increased from the estimated minimum of one trap per 15ha to one trap per 6.25ha, set out as 16 traps per 1km square. At this density even the smallest polecat home range recorded in Britain (16ha - see Section 8) was likely to contain at least two traps. Regular spacing of traps was ensured by placing a grid of 16 cells, each representing 250m by 250m, over a map of the 1km sampling square (see Figure 6.2). On the ground, one trap was placed in each cell at a site judged most likely to encounter a polecat (see Section 6.2.3.1).

56

Figure 6.1. Numbers of 1km squares of the Ordnance Survey grid occupied by 13 polecats over 17 radio-tracking sessions (see Section 6.2.1.1 for definition of main squares).

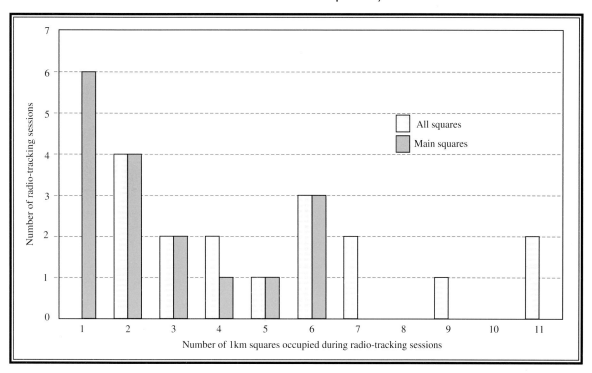

Figure 6.2. The 1km square trapping system showing an example of the distribution of traps (x) across 16 cells.

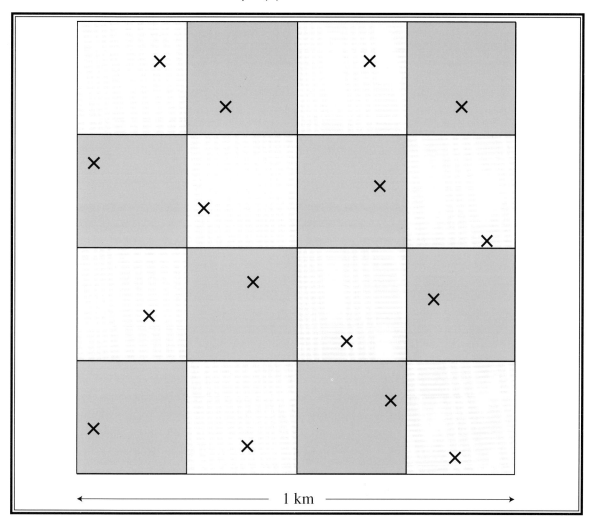

This pattern was tested in two 1km squares in Cardiganshire and Herefordshire in September 1993. Both caught polecats by the third day of trapping.

6.2.1.2 Duration of trapping sessions

In a sampling system designed to reflect variations in the abundance of a wide-ranging species, the ideal duration of sampling sessions is indicated by the point at which few new individuals are likely to be encountered. Figure 6.3 shows how visits to 1km squares of the OS grid by radio-tagged polecats accumulated during tracking sessions. While a small minority (<10%) of 1km squares were not visited until after day 20, over 60% (and more than 80% of main squares) had been visited by day ten. Thus, although polecats might take an excessive time, in terms of ideal trapping duration, to reveal all the 1km squares they occupy, an encouraging majority of squares are visited within a more manageable period.

Ultimately the length of sampling period had to be decided with the volunteers in mind. Given the amount of work involved and the likelihood of low trapping success, it was considered unreasonable to ask volunteers to participate in trapping sessions longer than one week. So the sampling system was based upon 16 traps set for seven days, giving a potential trapping effort per square of 112 trap-nights. Figure 6.3 suggests a 64% probability that a main 1km square would be visited by resident polecats during a seven-day trapping session. Since the aim was not to encounter every individual, but merely to sample populations in ways that might reflect variations in abundance, the seven-day duration seemed acceptable on this evidence.

6.2.1.3 The trapping season

The timing of the trapping season and its duration were chosen to maximise the probability of encountering polecats, while avoiding those periods when excessive movement in the population might distort results, such as the mating season and when juveniles disperse. Blandford and Walton (1991a) indicated that polecat mating activity occurs mainly in April, and juvenile dispersal takes place mainly in October. In the VWT radio-tracking study, however, all juveniles trapped and radio-tracked in late September and October were settled in stable home ranges, suggesting that most polecat dispersal occurs rather earlier than October in the west of England. This pattern was also reflected in the VWT road casualty data in Section 5 (see Figure 5.3a), which show a peak in records in September, rather than October (the fact that polecat records of all categories peak in October is explained by the contribution of records in that month from this trapping study). Bearing these facts in mind, a six-month trapping window was chosen in the 'winter' half of the year, from October to March inclusive. This ensured that the polecat population was at or close to its annual maximum, while avoiding both periods of population instability. Trapping was carried out over five winters, from 1993/94 to 1997/98, with each sample square trapped once over this period.

6.2.1.4 Selection of sample squares

Other mammal monitoring exercises based upon 1km squares have tended to adopt a stratified, random approach to ensure proportional coverage of, for example, different ITE Land Classes (eg. Hutchings & Harris, 1996; Wilson, et al., 1997). In the VWT study, an important consideration was the need for volunteers to check traps on seven consecutive mornings. This was a major constraint on square selection because many randomly pre-selected squares would not be matched with willing volunteers living close enough to operate them. This was especially true in a large proportion of the polecat's historical stronghold in rural Wales, where human population densities are relatively very low. In order to overcome this constraint, squares were not selected randomly, but were chosen in consultation with potential volunteers over as wide a geographical and landscape range as possible. As a general rule, sample 1km squares were sought which ensured that they:

1. Lay within the known range of the polecat in Britain.
2. Contained predominantly rural landscapes.
3. Avoided gamekeepered estates and other areas of heavy predator control.
4. Covered as wide an area as possible between the historical core and the fringe of the polecat's present range.

Beyond these constraints, squares were selected to suit the convenience of volunteers. In most cases they were close to either their homes or places of work, so that traps could easily be checked early in the morning.

6.2.2 The involvement of volunteers

Because live-trapping for carnivores is very labour intensive, involving volunteers was essential to the success of this sampling system. Britain is unique for the number of its competent amateur naturalists who contribute hugely to the recording and monitoring of many wildlife groups, including mammals. Volunteers were sought to help with polecat-trapping among the members of County Wildlife Trusts and local Natural History Groups. Despite the substantial commitment required, amounting to a day spent training and trap-setting, followed by seven subsequent mornings of checking traps for between one and three hours, the chance of seeing a live polecat at close quarters was, fortunately, sufficient incentive to recruit the people needed. Before finally committing themselves, volunteers were given a written explanation of the reasons for the live-trapping exercise and the scale of their role within it. Each volunteer was asked to:

1. Select a 1km square in consultation with the VWT staff.
2. Negotiate permission for access and trapping from all landowners in the square.
3. Assist the VWT staff with trap-setting on the agreed starting date.
4. Check traps on seven consecutive days; process and release all captures.
5. Record all trapping data on a simple form.
6. Help to collect all traps on the final day.

Volunteers were supplied with copies of the VWT's leaflet on polecats for distribution to landowners and other interested persons. During the day when traps were first set out, each volunteer was fully trained in the operation and re-baiting of the traps, and the weighing, marking and releasing of any polecats caught (see Section 6.2.3.3). Some squares were trapped by groups of three or more volunteers, who shared the tasks of setting and checking traps.

The polecat is listed on Schedule 6 of the Wildlife & Countryside Act 1981, so a licence is required if one intends trapping it. Each volunteer was supplied with a copy of a licence from the appropriate authority, together with a covering letter appointing him or her as a duly accredited agent. All were also given an Ordnance Survey 1:10,000 scale map of the relevant square and a contact telephone number to use in case of problems encountered during the trapping session. Each volunteer was telephoned two or three days into a trapping session to check that all was well.

6.2.3 The live-trapping protocol

6.2.3.1 Trap-setting

The 16-cell grid was drawn onto a map of each sample square. A single trap site was chosen in each 250m x 250m cell at a place thought most likely to catch a polecat. Sites were mainly in field margins, the base of hedges, farm buildings, by streams and ditches or in woodland edges. Radio-tracking had suggested that these were preferred habitats (see Section 8). Where necessary, trap sites were chosen so as to avoid the risk of interference by people or domestic animals. Setting 16 traps in a 1km square normally took 4-5 hours.

Figure 6.3. Cumulative occupancy of 1km squares by polecats over 17 radio-tracking sessions (see Section 6.2.1.1 for definition of main squares).

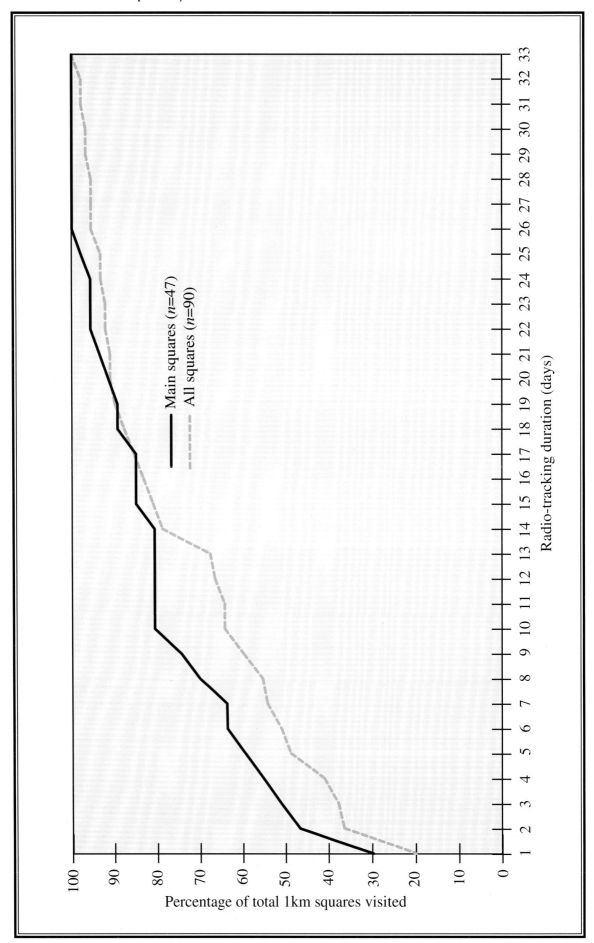

60

This study used single-entry cage traps designed for mink[3]. Each measured approximately 76 x 15 x 15cm, was made from metal mesh and had a sprung door at one end. The traps could conveniently be hidden from view in well-vegetated sites. As well as using local vegetation for camouflage, traps were first covered with dry hay as an important welfare measure. Polecats pulled at this soft, more yielding material instead of damaging themselves by attacking the wire mesh of the trap. Usually, they pulled large amounts of hay inside the trap and hid amongst it. Polecats trapped in such hay-covered traps appeared relatively unstressed compared with those caught in uncovered traps, and were frequently asleep in the hay when discovered.

When setting traps, great care was taken to ensure that hay and other materials could not interfere with the treadle mechanism or stop the door from closing fully, as experience had shown that polecats could escape from traps with incompletely closed doors. Proper door closure was confirmed by depressing the treadle several times before leaving the trap set.

Once set, every trap was baited with a single, dead, day-old chick culled as surplus stock by the poultry industry. Volunteers were given 16+ frozen chicks with which to re-bait traps on the fourth morning of trap-checking, regardless of the condition of the first chick provided.

6.2.3.2 Trap-checking

All traps were checked by volunteers as early as possible in the morning. A full check of 16 traps by one person took one to three hours depending on the terrain, the level of vehicle access and the fitness of the volunteer. A second check later in the day was thought unnecessary because polecats rarely move about during daylight (see Section 8). Traps were checked from a distance of a few metres, if possible, to avoid leaving fresh human scent. Traps were approached closely only if they appeared to have caught something, if they had been disturbed (foxes, badgers and livestock occasionally interfered with traps), or if re-baiting was required.

6.2.3.3 Processing trapped animals

When a trap was found to have caught an animal, the volunteer used a tent peg carefully to remove some of the covering material and lift the trap out of cover. Polecats or mink had usually filled the trap with hay (see Plate 7). This was parted gently with the tent peg in order to confirm the species caught. Animals other than polecats were released immediately by locking the trap door open while keeping the captive at the rear of the trap by insertion of a wooden, fingered 'comb' developed by Chanin (1976). When a polecat had been caught, it was weighed and marked before release.

The purpose of weighing was to determine the sex of animals trapped. Polecats are sexually dimorphic. Figure 6.4 shows that the body weights of 62 live-trapped or road-killed animals, sexed by other means, showed very limited overlap between males and females between October and March inclusive. Only one 100g bodyweight category, 951-1050g, included animals of both sexes, and only three animals (4.8%) fell into the larger, intermediate range of 951-1150g. So, accurate bodyweights recorded by volunteers could be used to determine the sex of most of the polecats trapped. Animals were weighed inside the traps by hooking the trap onto a 5kg Salter spring balance[4]. Sometimes material had to be removed from the trap first so that the total weight did not exceed the capacity of the balance. Weighing was easiest if the spring balance was attached to one end of the trap; if the balance was attached to the middle of the trap, the trap tended to 'see-saw' in response to the animal's movements. After the polecat had been released, the weight of the empty trap was subtracted from the overall weight, taking care to ensure that the trap contained the same quantity of hay and debris as on the first weighing.

After weighing, a short-term coloured mark was applied to the animal's fur so that any animal recaptured subsequently could be identified. This was done with a non-toxic aerosol

[3] Supplied by A. Fenn & Co., Hoopers Lane, Astwood Bank, Redditch, Worcestershire B96 6AR, UK.
[4] Salter Industrial Measurement Ltd., George Street, West Bromwich, West Midlands B70 6AD, UK.

Figure 6.4. Distribution of bodyweights of road casualty and live-trapped polecats of known sex from Wales, Herefordshire and Worcestershire, October-March, 1993-1997 (*n*=62).

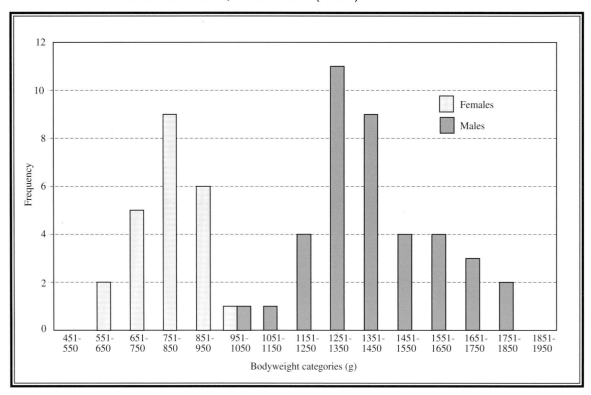

spray[5] applied to the fur of the back through the mesh of the trap. To minimise stress, animals were encouraged to remain largely concealed among the hay in the trap while the spray was applied. Red and blue sprays were especially effective at leaving a mark in the soft, yellow underfur, which is long and thick in the polecat's winter coat. On the few occasions when several polecats were trapped in the same square, sprays of different colours were applied, or marks of the same colour were applied at different places on each animal's body. Over longer trapping periods these coloured marks faded quite quickly on polecats, but were still visible on animals retrapped after ten days. Thus, they were adequate for this study based on a seven-day trapping period.

During weighing and marking the volunteers behaved quietly and calmly, moving slowly around the animal in the trap so as not to alarm it. This precaution, and allowing polecats to hide among the hay inside the trap, served to reduce stress for both animals and volunteers. On the few occasions when these precautions were not taken, frightened polecats tended to release a pungent scent from their anal glands while 'waggling' their tails to spread the stink. Exceptionally, stressed animals made a sharp, threatening 'chack' sound. Weighing and marking usually took less than ten minutes. Animals were released into cover at their site of capture immediately afterwards. To avoid the risk of immediately catching the same animal again, each trap was left closed for one night after catching a polecat. It was then reset and re-baited on the following morning. Typically, trapped polecats did not eat the bait provided.

6.2.3.4 Recording habitat and prey data

Rabbits and their burrows are known to be important to polecats, as a source of prey and resting sites (see Section 8). Since variations in rabbit abundance might affect the numbers of polecats, an attempt was made to quantify this factor in each square by counting all 'active' rabbit burrow entrances visible from the route walked to set the traps. This provided a crude index of rabbit abundance within each sample square with which the polecat data could be compared. During analysis, sample squares were lumped into three classes of rabbit abundance (high, medium and low - see Section 6.3.6.1).

[5] Stock-marker spray from Ritchey Tagg Ltd., Masham, Near Ripon, N. Yorks. HG4 4ES, UK.

An index of habitat complexity was derived from the map of each 1km square by counting the number of times the lines of the 16-cell grid intersected linear habitat features (eg. streams, roads, hedges, walls) and habitat boundaries such as the edges of woodlands, moors and marshes.

A range of other geographical variables was derived from maps, including altitudinal range, extent of woodland and wetland, length of woodland edge and the number of farmsteads. A score for road density was derived for each square by measuring the total length of 'A' and 'M' class roads in a 3 x 3km square block (ie. 9 x 1km^2) with the trapped square at its centre.

All sample squares were categorised according to their position relative to the polecat's historical stronghold. Langley and Yalden (1977) noted 11 counties in Wales and along the English border where the polecat had not become extinct during the 19th or early 20th centuries. Squares trapped in these counties were termed 'historical core' squares. Langley and Yalden (1977) also recognised counties where the polecat was believed to have become extinct (see Appendix 1); squares trapped in these counties were termed 'fringe' squares. The system of county boundaries adopted by Langley and Yalden (1977) corresponds closely with the system of vice-counties used in this section (see Figure 5.1)

6.2.4 The Ledbury study

To aid an interpretation of the data generated by the 1km square sampling exercise, an intensive study was carried out in one of the sample squares near Ledbury in Herefordshire (an 'historical core' county). This square included a stretch of the A449 road between Malvern and Ledbury where many (15+ per year) polecats are reported to the VWT as road casualties or live sightings. The Ledbury square was trapped in each month of the six-month trapping window between October 1997 and March 1998. The standard protocol was altered slightly by lengthening the trapping period from seven days to ten. By this means it was hoped to test the effect of an extended trapping period on the quality and quantity of the data. To ease identification of animals from one month to the next, all polecats trapped in this exercise were permanently marked with sub-cutaneous 'identichips'[6]. With the exception of the first seven days in the first trapping session (in October 1997), no data from this exercise were used in the analysis of the main sample of trapped squares.

6.3 Results

6.3.1 The number and distribution of sample squares

Trapping was carried out during the five winters of 1993/94 to 1997/98. Over this period 136 1km squares were trapped once each for polecats according to the protocol described above (97% of squares were trapped in the first four winters). Two further squares were abandoned after traps had been set - due to a heavy fall of snow in one case, and the theft of most of the traps in the other (the thief followed the volunteers' footprints in snow in order to find the traps). Approximately 150 volunteer trappers operated the scheme, some of whom operated three or more squares over the five-winter period. Nearly 15,000 trap days were completed, where one trap day = one trap set for one day.

The trapped squares were widely distributed throughout the polecat's British range (see Figure 6.5). Most (95.6%) were located in Wales or the English Midlands, but six squares were trapped in Cumbria where a reintroduced population is well-established (see Section 5.3.5.5). Sample squares were situated in 107 10km squares of the OS grid and in 25 Watsonian vice-counties. The 11 'historical core' vice-counties (as defined in Section 6.2.3.4) contained 82 squares, compared with 54 sample squares in 14 'fringe' vice-counties. These vice-counties are listed in Table 6.1. The availability of volunteers had a considerable influence on the distribution of sample squares, with some vice-counties containing fewer trapped squares than intended because there were too few volunteers to cover them.

[6] Animalcare Ltd., Dunnington, York, UK.

Figure 6.5a. Location of 136 1km squares trapped for polecats, 1993-1998.

Figure 6.5b. Location of 107 10km squares containing trapping squares.

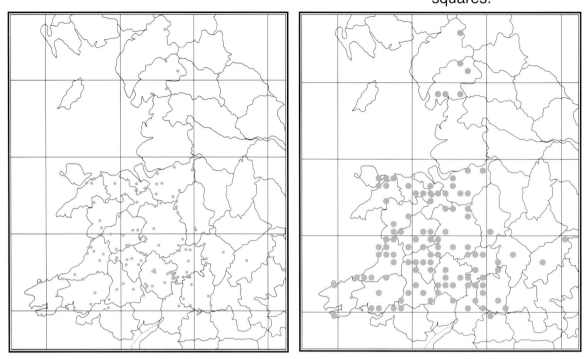

The sample squares were distributed across 19 ITE Land Classes. Within the polecat's 'historical core' the distribution of sample squares broadly reflected the proportions of Land Classes available in Wales and the West Midlands of England. In the 'fringe' area, however, the number of available Land Classes was much greater, so the proportional match with the distribution of sample squares was less close.

6.3.2 Numbers of polecats trapped

Polecats were trapped in 66 (48.5%) of the 136 squares sampled. These are referred to as 'positive' squares. Figure 6.6 shows how many separate individual polecats were caught per sampling square, and how many captures of polecats were made (figures for captures include all recaptures of individuals within a sampling period; thus, the number of captures exceeds the number of individuals recorded). In over half (56.1%) of the positive squares only a single individual was caught and only a single capture was made (53% of positive squares). Exceptionally, more than four individuals (10.6% of positive squares) and more than six captures (15.1%) were recorded. The rate of recapture of individuals over the 7-day trapping period was low, with 30 recaptures recorded among the 123 individuals marked. Only 13 (19.7%) positive squares recorded recaptures within the sampling period. One of these squares was in east Cumbria, in an area where the trapped animals showed phenotypic evidence of cross-breeding with feral ferrets (see Section 7.7) and a tendency towards 'trap-happiness'. One male in this square accounted for 20% of recaptures across all squares sampled. This animal was trapped on every day of the seven-day session, despite the volunteer trapper following instructions to close traps for one night after each capture. In the intensively studied square near Ledbury there were 13 captures of six individuals. Further study revealed this to be an area of exceptionally high polecat activity (see Section 6.3.8).

Fewer than ten escapes by polecats from traps were recorded. These usually involved animals pulling on the door and spring mechanism so powerfully that the metal became bent and twisted, allowing escape. In one case an animal escaped through the roof of a trap by removing a single length of mesh. The strong smell and presence of polecat fur confirmed the identity of these escapees.

Figure 6.6. Frequency of occurrence of trapping squares generating different numbers of individuals and captures (see Section 6.3.2 for definition of individuals and captures).

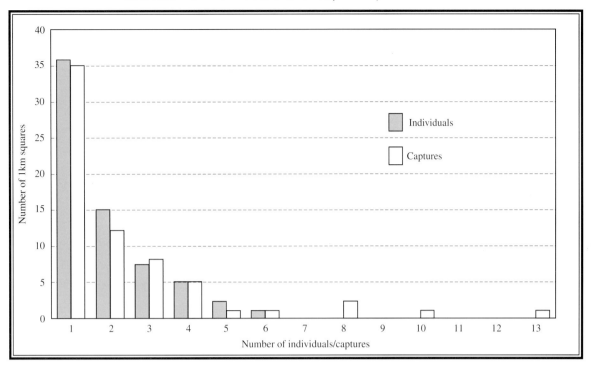

Considering all sampling squares together, a polecat was just as likely to be caught on any one of the seven days of trapping sessions (see Figure 6.7a). There was no significant variation in the timing of capture of new individuals over the seven days trapped (Chi-square $= 2.83$, $df = 6$, $p > 0.05$). This suggests that, as predicted in Section 6.2.1.2, the trapping period was too short to encounter all polecats that may have been present (with a much longer trapping period one might expect a progressive reduction in the number of new individuals caught as all available animals were encountered). The pattern of captures suggests that polecats were not deterred by fresh human scent, since new captures were just

Plate 6. *Volunteers Chris Bradley and John Evans setting cage traps near Kinlet in south Shropshire, November 1995. This 1km square recorded three captures of two polecats. Volunteer effort was critical to the success of the trapping study.*

Figure 6.7a. Frequency distribution of all new polecat captures (*n*=123) over the 136 seven-day trapping sessions.

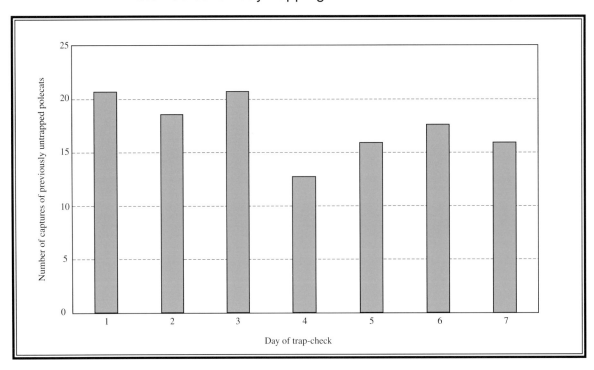

as likely to occur on those days following close human contact with traps (day 1 after trap-setting, and day 5 after re-baiting). Of the 66 positive squares, nearly half (48.5%) had recorded captures by the second day of trap-checking, although 10.6% were blank until the very last day (see Figure 6.7b).

Using the bodyweight method of determining sex (see Section 6.2.3.3), the 123 animals trapped comprised 96 males and 27 females, a sex ratio of 3.56 males per female. This 'winter only' sample differs from the male to female ratio of 2.4:1 in a year-round sample of road casualties (see Section 5.3.2.1). This difference might reflect the exclusion of the mid-summer period of high adult female activity from the winter trapping window. As a

Figure 6.7b. The number of days to the first capture of a polecat in positive sample squares (*n*=66).

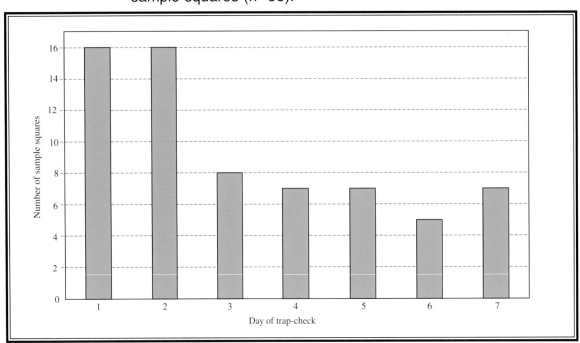

proportion of the total number of individuals trapped of each sex, female recaptures comprised 22.2% and male recaptures 25% (42% of all male recaptures occurred in just two squares in Cumbria). Thus, although males dominated the number of individuals recorded, both sexes appeared equally likely to re-enter traps during the trapping period.

6.3.3 Geographical variation in trapping success

Trapping results are summarised in Table 6.1 and Figure 6.8, lumped by vice-counties. A positive ranking correlation was found between the proportion of positive squares in each vice-county and the mean number of individuals trapped per square (r_s=0.67, n=18, p<0.01). This suggests that, in vice-counties where there are more polecats, the 1km square sampling method is more likely to encounter them and to record them in greater numbers. Although this may seem an obvious conclusion, it is important because it confirms the value of the chosen trapping protocol.

Plate 7. *Volunteer Pam Blaxland with hay-filled trap indicating a polecat capture, near Welshpool, Montgomeryshire, March 1996.*

6.3.3.1 The influence of the 'historical core'

The positive squares where polecats were caught were not evenly distributed across the entire sampling area. Polecats were marginally more likely to be caught in the 'historical core' than in the 'fringe' vice-counties (Yates' corrected Chi square=4.0 df=1, p<0.05). Although sample squares in the 'historical core' tended to record more individuals and captures than 'fringe' squares, these differences were not significant at the 5% level (individuals per square: t=-1.374, df=134, p>0.1; captures per square: t=0.869, df=134, p>0.1). This suggests that these values covered too limited a range for any regional trends to be apparent.

6.3.3.2 Defining the 'current core' and 'current fringe' of the polecat's range

The association between trapping success on the one hand and 'historical core' and 'fringe' areas on the other was so slight that it limits the value of using historical factors to predict the present core of the polecat's range. Figure 6.8 shows the variation between vice-counties in the proportion of squares in which polecats were caught. Polecats were most likely to be caught in north-west Wales, Radnor, and the English border counties of Chester, Salop, and Hereford. Sampling squares in these areas were almost twice as likely to record polecats than the remainder.

These broad variations in trapping success can be used to define more accurately the current stronghold of the polecat. There were some difficulties in approaching this task objectively on the basis of trapping success alone. For example, the Welsh vice-county of Flint revealed a success rate of 33.3% positive squares, yet it is sandwiched between two vice-counties which revealed 60% or more. Likewise, Brecon revealed only 33.3% positive,

Table 6.1. A summary of polecat trapping results from 1km squares sampled between winters 1993/94 and 1997/98. See Section 6.3.2 for definition of 'individuals' and 'captures'. 'Current core' vice-counties as defined in Section 6.3.2 are shown in capital letters.

Vice-county	Number of squares trapped	Number of +ve squares	Number of trap-nights	Number of polecats trapped	Male:female ratio	Mean individuals per square	Mean individuals per +ve square	Number of polecat captures	Mean captures per square	Mean captures per +ve square
'Historical core'										
CAERNARVON	8	5	892	12	5:1	1.5	2.4	13	1.625	2.6
DENBIGH	5	3	555	5	5:0	1.0	1.7	6	1.2	2.0
MERIONETH	3	2	333	4	0.33:1	1.33	2.0	4	1.33	2.0
MONTGOMERY	9	4	1,006	5	5:0	0.55	1.25	5	0.55	1.25
CARDIGAN	9	4	989	7	6:1	0.77	1.75	9	1.0	2.25
RADNOR	8	5	882	14	1.33:1	1.75	2.8	17	2.125	3.4
CARMARTHEN	5	3	573	4	3:1	0.8	1.33	5	1.0	1.67
BRECON	6	2	670	3	2:1	0.5	1.5	3	0.5	1.5
Pembroke	2	0	221	0	-	-	-	0	-	-
SALOP	11	7	1,172	11	10:1	1.0	1.57	13	1.18	1.86
HEREFORD	16	11	1,767	19	5.3:1	1.19	1.73	27	1.69	2.45
All 'historical core' squares	82 (56.1%)	46	9,060	84	3.67:1	1.02±0.14	1.83±0.18	102	1.24±0.22	2.22±0.33
'Historical fringe'										
FLINT	3	1	322	2	2:0	0.67	2.0	2	0.67	2.0
Glamorgan	3	0	336	0	-	-	-	0	-	-
Monmouth	1	0	108	0	-	-	-	0	-	-
Cumberland	1	0	112	0	-	-	-	0	-	-
Westmorland	5	2	541	8	8:0	1.6	4.0	18	2.25	9.0
CHESTER	8	5	886	6	5:1	0.75	1.2	6	0.75	1.2
Stafford	4	2	443	2	2:0	0.5	1.0	2	0.5	1.0
Worcester	15	7	1,609	16	1:1	1.1	2.28	17	1.13	2.43
West Gloucester	3	0	336	0	-	-	-	0	-	-
East Gloucester	4	0	448	0	-	-	-	0	-	-
Warwick	3	1	331	1	1:0	0.33	1.0	1	0.33	1.0
Northampton	2	1	222	2	2:0	1.0	2.0	3	1.5	3.0
Oxford	1	1	110	2	2:0	2.0	2.0	2	2.0	2.0
North Wilts	1	0	112	0	-	-	-	0	-	-
All 'fringe' squares	54 (37.0%)	20	5,916	39	3.33:1	0.72	1.95±0.25	51	0.95±0.26	2.55±0.55
All squares	136 (48.5%)	66	14,976	123	3.5:1	0.9±0.11	1.86±0.15	153	1.125±0.17	2.32±0.28

yet it is an 'historical core' county adjacent to others which revealed 60% or more. Despite their low trapping success, it was decided to include both Flint and Brecon in the 'current core' because of their proximity to high success counties, their relatively long occupation by polecats, and because polecats are known to be common in both. Conversely, in the English 'fringe' vice-counties of Stafford and Worcester trapping success exceeded that of both Flint and Brecon, yet it was decided to classify them as 'current fringe' counties because of their more recent recolonisation by polecats. A block of 12 relatively high trapping success vice-counties was identified as the 'current core' of the polecat's British range. These (Caernarvon, Denbigh, Flint, Chester, Merioneth, Montgomery, Salop, Cardigan, Radnor, Brecon, Carmarthen and Hereford) are shown in colour in Figure 6.8. The remainder are termed the 'current fringe'. It should be stressed that using vice-county boundaries to define these areas is a relatively crude approach because it is bound to mask more local variations in polecat abundance.

No significant differences were apparent in the mean number of individuals or captures recorded per positive square between 'current core' and 'current fringe' vice-counties (see Table 6.2). This suggests that, although polecats are recorded in significantly fewer sample squares in the 'current fringe', where they do occur they are generally no less abundant when compared with the 'current core'. Thus, a possible difference between polecat populations in the 'current core' and 'current fringe' areas is a more patchy distribution in the latter. 'Current fringe' vice-counties were represented among those trapping squares recording the most polecats. For example, the eight squares in which four or more individuals were trapped were located in Caernarvon, Cardigan, Radnor (2) and Hereford ('current core' vice-counties), and Cumbria (2) and Worcestershire ('current fringe').

Table 6.2. Mean numbers of individuals and captures recorded in positive sample squares in the 'current core' and 'current fringe' of the polecat's range.

	'Current core'	'Current fringe'	*t* value	*df*	*p* value
Mean individuals per positive square ± S.D.	1.8 ± 1.2	2.2 ± 1.2	-1.22	64	>0.22
Mean captures per positive square ± S.D.	2.1 ± 2.1	3.1 ± 2.8	-1.40	64	>0.16

The low trapping success encountered in much of south Wales is surprising, considering the proximity of this area to the polecat's historical stronghold. Indeed, on the evidence of trapping success, the species appears more strongly established in the English border vice-counties of Chester, Salop and Hereford, than in much of southern Wales.

6.3.4 Seasonal variation

Sample squares were trapped in roughly equal numbers in each of the six calendar months October – March. Although the proportion of positive squares varied between 66.6% in October and 25% in January (see Figure 6.9), there was apparently no significant association between the occurrence of positive and negative squares and the month of trapping (Chi-square=9.18, df=5, p>0.05). A lack of statistical power due to the small sample size in some months may explain this apparent lack of association. Figure 6.9 compares the monthly occurrence of positive squares with data from the VWT's widespread 1990s road casualty recording (see Section 5) and radio-tracking (see Section 8). These three independent sets of

Figure 6.8. An estimate of the current 'core' of the polecat's main range, based mainly on variations in the proportion of positive trapping squares by vice-county.

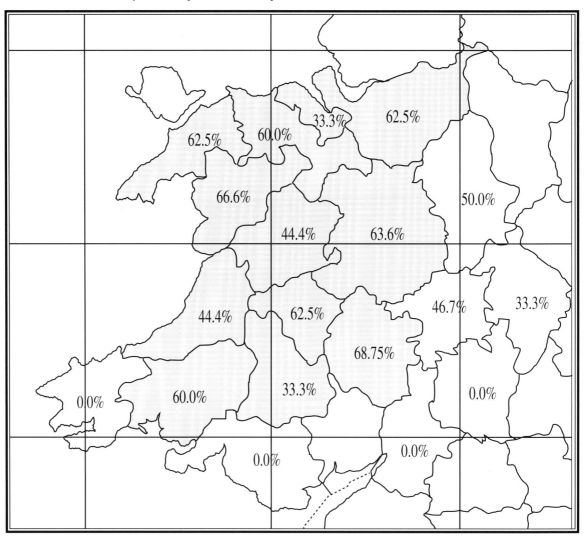

Figure 6.9. Comparison of monthly variations in polecat trapping success with two independent measures of activity.

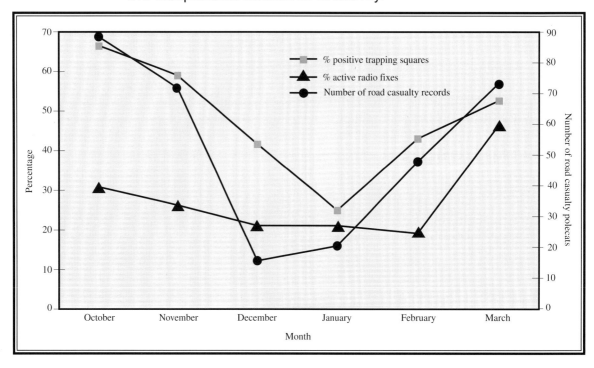

70

data suggest a low point in polecat activity in mid-winter. The changing proportion of positive trapping squares corresponds particularly well with the number of road casualty records received per month by the VWT ($r=0.87$, $n=6$, $p<0.05$). This suggests that the monthly variation in trapping success reflects the general pattern of polecat activity.

6.3.5 Associations with habitat variables

Variations in the numbers of individuals and captures recorded in sample squares were compared with the range of habitat variables derived from the maps of sample squares (see Section 6.2.3.4). All the correlation coefficients calculated for these comparisons failed to reach significance, suggesting that none of the habitat variables had a powerful influence on the number of polecats recorded in the squares (see Table 6.3). Roads as a habitat variable are considered separately in Section 6.3.6.2.

Table 6.3. Correlation statistics for habitat variables in sample squares against the number of individual polecats and captures in squares ($n=136$).

Habitat variable quantified in sample squares	Correlation with number of individuals	Correlation with number of captures
Habitat complexity index	$r=0.05$, $p>0.52$	$r=0.05$, $p>0.57$
Area of woodland	$r=0.06$, $p>0.47$	$r=0.08$, $p>0.35$
Length of woodland edge	$r=0.01$, $p>0.87$	$r=0.03$, $p>0.75$
Number of farmsteads	$r=0.09$, $p>0.30$	$r=0.07$, $p>0.41$
Length of running water	$r=0.05$, $p>0.55$	$r=0.03$, $p>0.74$
Area of standing water	$r=0.07$, $p>0.39$	$r=0.08$, $p>0.33$
Number of ponds	$r=0.06$, $p>0.44$	$r=0.07$, $p>0.37$
Number of woods	$r=0.06$, $p>0.48$	$r=0.03$, $p>0.68$

6.3.6 Associations with other variables

6.3.6.1 Rabbit abundance

There was an association between the probability of trapping polecats in a square and the index of rabbit abundance in that square. Polecats were more likely to be caught in squares with 'medium' (20-99 active burrows) or 'high' (100+ burrows) rabbit indices than in those classed as 'low' (<20 burrows) (Yates' corrected Chi-square=7.72, $df=1$, $p<0.01$). Furthermore, a Spearman Rank correlation between the three categories of rabbit abundance and the number of individual polecats trapped revealed a significant positive correlation ($r=0.261$, $p<0.01$, $n=136$).

This association between polecats and rabbits differed between the 'current core' and 'current fringe' of the polecat's range (see Table 6.4). It was especially strong in the 'current core' in respect of polecat captures. Conversely, there was apparently no significant correlation between indices of rabbit adundance and numbers of polecats in the 'current fringe'. Thus, the association between rabbits and polecats apparent over the whole sample of 136 squares seems to result entirely from the strong correlation within the 'current core' of the polecat's range.

Table 6.4. Correlation between rabbits and polecats in the 'current core' and 'current fringe' of the latter's range. *Variables: number of polecat captures (ie. including recaptures) in sample squares, number of individual polecats, number of 'active' rabbit burrows counted.*

Variables	Correlation statistic	Sample size	*p* value
'Current core'			
polecat captures v. rabbits	$r=0.26$	$n=91$	<0.05*
individual polecats v. rabbits	$r=0.19$	$n=91$	>0.07
'Current fringe'			
polecat captures v. rabbits	$r=0.14$	$n=45$	>0.34
individual polecats v. rabbits	$r=0.19$	$n=45$	>0.21

6.3.6.2 The influence of road density

The distribution of both positive squares and numbers of polecats recorded per square were compared with the density of main roads. Each group of 9 x 1km^2 squares with a sample square at its centre (see Section 6.2.3.4) was assigned to one of two road density categories. These were 'high road density' (>1km of 'M' or 'A' class roads) and 'low density' (1km or less of such roads). Table 6.5 shows the results of the first of these comparisons, examined by calculating Chi-square for association between them. When all 136 sampling squares were considered together there was no association between road density and positive squares; this was also true for the 91 squares in the 'current core' of the species' range. By contrast, there was an inverse association between these variables in the 45 squares of the 'current fringe'.

Table 6.5. The association between high and low main road density (see above) and positive and negative sample squares (examined by Yates' corrected Chi-square).

Sampling unit	Number of positive squares, high road density	Number of positive squares, low road density	Chi-square	*df*	*p* value
'Current core'	31	19	0.15	1	>0.5
(91 squares)	(55.4%)	(57.6%)			
'Current fringe'	4	12	6.57	1	<0.05*
(45 squares)	(14.8%)	(55.6%)			
All squares	35	31	2.83	1	>0.09
($n=136$)	(42.2%)	(58.5%)			

Table 6.6 shows the results of a second comparison, based on correlation coefficients for the three variables. In this comparison the total length of main roads ('M' and 'A' class) in the group of nine 1km squares that had a trapping square at its centre was used. There was a negative correlation between road length and the number of individuals trapped in sample squares in the 'current fringe', but not in the 'current core', of the polecat's range. No correlations were apparent between the number of captures and road length.

Table 6.6. Correlation between number of polecats caught (captures and individuals) and length of main roads (in nine 1km squares surrounding trapping squares) in the 'current core' and 'current fringe' of the polecat's range. (*Statistically significant correlation.)

Variables	Correlation	Sample size	p value
'Current core'			
Road length v. number of individuals	$r=0.06$	$n=91$	>0.5
Road length v. number of captures	$r=0.6$	$n=91$	>0.5
'Current fringe'			
Road length v. number of individuals	$r=-0.3$	$n=45$	<0.05*
Road length v. number of captures	$r=-0.1$	$n=45$	>0.47

6.3.7 Non-target captures

Several species of animal were caught accidentally while trapping for polecats. They totalled 153 individuals spread over 74 sample squares. In 38 squares they were the only animals trapped. They were dominated by four species; in order of abundance these were feral cats, grey squirrels, rabbits and feral mink. Other occasional captures were of common rats, a pheasant and a juvenile otter. No association was found between those squares recording non-target species and those recording polecats (Yates' corrected Chi-square=0.02, $df=1$, $p>0.5$).

6.3.8 The Ledbury study

Fortuitously, the square chosen for this study emerged as the most successful, in terms of numbers of polecats caught, of all the 136 squares sampled. Ten individual polecats were live-trapped on 58 occasions over the six months of the study. All were fitted with identichips in the first two months of trapping. No new animals were recorded in the subsequent four months of trapping, suggesting a stable population with no detectable immigration. The data from this intensively studied square compare very favourably with those from the remaining 135 squares. 13 captures of six individuals recorded over the first seven days of trapping in October 1997 exceeds the numbers recorded in any other square. This record was itself exceeded in seven days trapping in the same square in November 1997, when 13 captures of nine individuals were recorded. Clearly the polecat population in the vicinity of the Ledbury square was unusually dense at the time of this study. Trapping data from the Ledbury study are summarised in Table 6.7.

Figure 6.10 shows the number of individuals and captures recorded for each of the six consecutive trapping months, and illustrates the effects upon these variables of extending each seven-day trapping session by three days. Polecats were trapped in every month, regardless of trapping duration; thus the Ledbury square was consistently 'positive'. Although several captures were recorded beyond the seventh day of trapping, only in one month (October 1997) was an animal trapped for the first time in the three-day period of extended trapping.

Table 6.7. A summary of the trapping results from ten-day sessions over six consecutive months in a single 1km square near Ledbury, Herefordshire. Captures identified with a larger **+** in bold occurred after the seventh day of trapping. 'Cells' refers to the division of the 1km square into 16 equal cells of 6.25ha.

Animal	October — Number of captures (& cells trapped in)	November — Number of captures (& cells trapped in)	December — Number of captures (& cells trapped in)	January — Number of captures (& cells trapped in)	February — Number of captures (& cells trapped in)	March — Number of captures (& cells trapped in)	Oct-March — Total number of cells trapped in	Status
Male 1	+++ (2)	++ (2)	++++ (4)	- (0)	- (0)	++ (2)	5	Main Resident
Male 2	++++ (2)	++++ (4)	+++ (3)	+ (1)	- (0)	- (0)	4	Main Resident
Male 3	+++ (3)	+++ (2)	+++ (4)	+ (1)	+ (1)	- (0)	4	Main Resident
Male 4	+ (1)	+ (1)	- (0)	- (0)	- (0)	- (0)	2	Peripheral Resident
Female 1	++++ (4)	+++ (2)	+++ (3)	- (0)	- (0)	- (0)	5	Main Resident
Female 2	+ (1)	++ (1)	- (0)	- (0)	- (0)	- (0)	2	Peripheral Resident
Female 3	+ (1)	- (0)	- (0)	- (0)	- (0)	- (0)	1	Periph. Res./ Transient?
Female 4	- (0)	+ (1)	+ (1)	- (0)	- (0)	- (0)	1	Peripheral Resident
Female 5	- (0)	+ (1)	- (0)	- (0)	- (0)	- (0)	1	Periph. Res./ Transient?
Female 6	- (0)	+ (1)	+ (1)	- (0)	- (0)	- (0)	2	Peripheral Resident

Figure 6.10a. The number of polecat captures in the Ledbury square, over seven and ten days trapping duration.

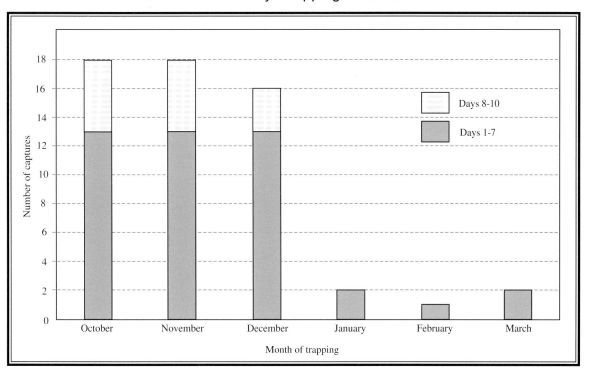

Figure 6.10b. Numbers of individuals trapped in the Ledbury square, over seven and ten days trapping duration.

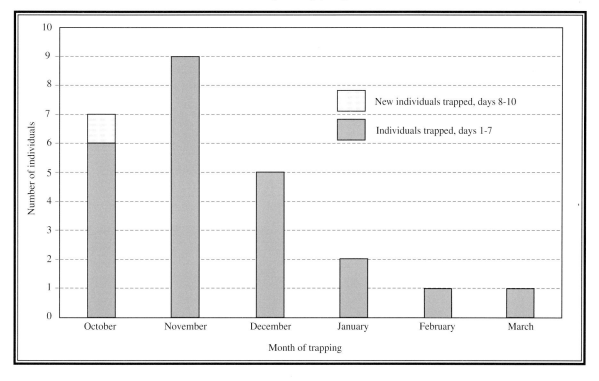

Thus, extending the trapping period to ten days had no influence upon the probability of catching any polecats, and almost no influence on the number of individuals recorded.

Figure 6.10 also illustrates the marked fall in numbers of captures and individuals recorded in the latter half of the six-month period in the Ledbury square (an effect not apparent in the remaining once-trapped 135 squares, though the proportion of positive squares did show a drop in mid-winter - see Figure 6.9). It is unclear whether this was due to emigration, mortality, or due to some change in the animals' behaviour such as reduced activity or increased trap-shyness. One cannot rule out trap-shyness as an influence in the

Plate 8. *The Ledbury square, Herefordshire, in which ten polecats were live-trapped on 58 occasions between October 1997 and March 1998. Of all 136 sampled, this 1km square recorded the greatest number of polecats trapped in seven days.*

Ledbury square, where frequently-trapped animals might have learned to avoid traps over the six-month window. It is unlikely to affect the main sample of squares because of their comparatively very brief trapping duration.

The frequency and location of 58 captures and recaptures of the ten individuals enabled an assessment of each animal's residency status in relation to the sample square (see Table 6.7). Individuals trapped in four or more of the 16 'cells' in the Ledbury square, and in three or more different months, were classed as 'main residents'. Four animals (three males and one female) fell into this category. The remaining six individuals were trapped in two or fewer months and in two or fewer peripheral cells only; these were classed as 'peripheral residents' or, in the case of females 3 and 5 which were trapped once only, as either 'peripheral residents' or 'possible transients'. Considering all trapping months, first captures of the four main residents occurred earlier in trapping sessions than did those of the other animals (mean number of days to first capture was 2.5 for main residents, compared with 4.89 days for the remainder; $t=2.634$, $df=25$, $p<0.05$). Therefore, it seems likely that the number of polecats trapped in other 1km squares in this sampling exercise was dominated by animals mainly resident in, rather than peripheral to, the sampling squares.

The distribution of all captures in relation to the 16 cells of the Ledbury square suggests a degree of range overlap over the six-month trapping period (see Figure 6.11). More than one individual was recorded in nine of the 14 cells in which polecats were trapped. Two male 'main residents' (males 1 and 2) were respectively recorded up to four times each in the same three cells (of the six they occupied in total), suggesting considerable range overlap.

6.4 Discussion

This attempt to develop a system for monitoring polecats in Britain was a step into the unknown, since there was no certainty at the outset that the data would meet basic

76

Figure 6.11. The distribution of 58 captures of ten polecats (M1-4, F1-6) over the 16 cells of the 1km square near Ledbury, Herefordshire. Numbers preceding the animal code indicate the total number of captures in that cell and, in brackets, the number of months in which that animal was trapped in the cell. All cells occupied by the four 'main residents' are shown in colour.

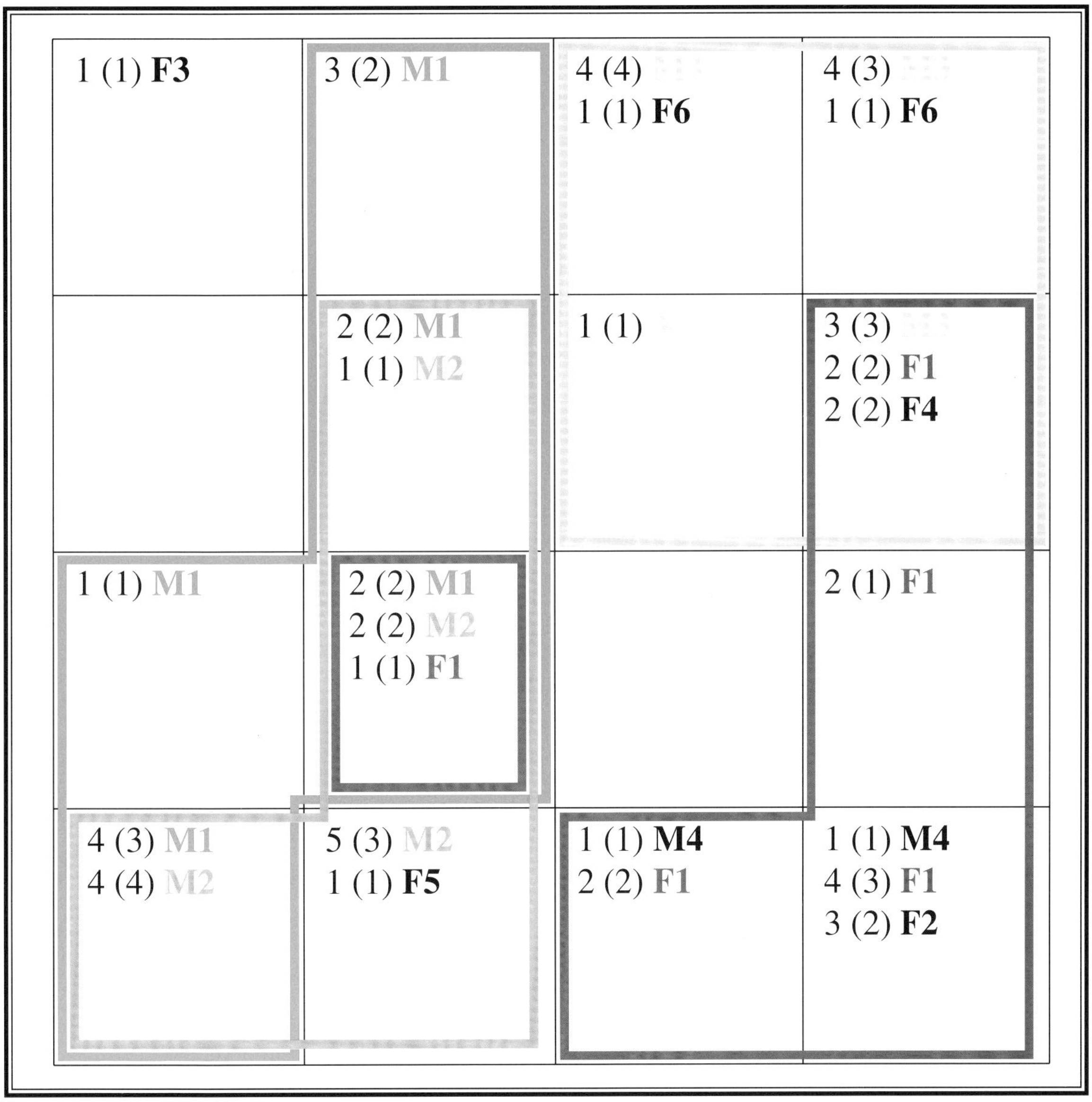

1 (1) **F3**	3 (2) M1	4 (4) 1 (1) **F6**	4 (3) 1 (1) **F6**
	2 (2) M1 1 (1) M2	1 (1)	3 (3) 2 (2) **F1** 2 (2) **F4**
1 (1) M1	2 (2) M1 2 (2) M2 1 (1) **F1**		2 (1) **F1**
4 (3) M1 4 (4) M2	5 (3) M2 1 (1) **F5**	1 (1) **M4** 2 (2) **F1**	1 (1) **M4** 4 (3) **F1** 3 (2) **F2**

monitoring requirements. Similar leaps of faith are anticipated in recommendations for other mammal species for which no tried and tested monitoring systems exist (Macdonald *et al.*, 1998). As predicted in Section 6.2, the sampling system adopted has many limitations arising out of the practical necessity to compromise heavily upon the ideal approach. Nevertheless, it is believed that the system has merits, and that the patterns emerging from the data are encouraging because they fit independent predictions about variations in polecat abundance. For example, the marked geographical variation in the likelihood of recording polecats in sample squares conforms with the expectation of greatest abundance in a core zone close to the species' historical stronghold.

6.4.1 Evaluation of the sampling method

The predictably low number of individuals and captures recorded per sample square places limits upon quantitative comparison between samples of squares. Thus, it was not possible to derive reliable indices of polecat activity or estimates of population density on a square-by-square basis in the manner of, for example, the national badger survey (Wilson *et al.*, 1997). In keeping with some other mammal surveys (eg. Strachan & Jefferies, 1996), the most useful quantitative measure was the proportion of positive sampling points in a given area. Since the probability of polecats being recorded in a sample square is a function of both local population density and the level of activity within the square, this variable can be assumed to relate to the degree to which polecats are established in an area.

The absence of any apparent influence of either local habitat variables or the month of trapping (within the six-month winter trapping 'window') upon the probability of squares catching polecats is advantageous from the monitoring viewpoint. It may obviate the need to control tightly for these two factors in future exercises. However, the evidence from other sources of a mid-winter reduction in polecat activity should not be ignored.

6.4.1.1 Negative squares

Caution is needed in drawing conclusions about the 70 squares (51.5% of the total) in which polecats were not recorded. Radio-tracking data presented in Section 6.2 suggest it is unsafe to infer that polecats are wholly absent from negative squares. Rather, it is more realistic to assume that polecats may be present in the vicinity, but that polecat activity within some squares is too low to be reflected in trapping results over a seven-day 'window'. This assumption was supported during the live-trapping study by the occasional occurrence of live sightings or road casualty records within or close to a number of negative squares.

6.4.1.2 The density of sample squares

The VWT exercise did not achieve an adequate density of sample squares in many parts of the polecat's range, largely because of an inevitable shortage of willing volunteers in areas where few people lived. For example, 11 of the 25 vice-counties covered contained three or fewer sample squares, making any comparisons of data at this scale unreliable. Current recommendations for mammal monitoring, proposed by Macdonald *et al.*, (1998), are based upon the 'QQ Grid' used in the national water vole survey (Strachan & Jefferies, 1996). This involves the random selection of five 1km squares from within each of 18 10km squares selected systematically (10km squares arranged in a pattern of alternating quincunxes and quartets, hence 'QQ') from each 100km square (Macdonald *et al.*, 1998, gives a full explanation). This represents a density of 90 1km squares in every 100km square, approximately four times the density achieved in the VWT study. To meet the ideal density of sample squares proposed by Macdonald *et al.*, (1998) would be feasible with professional trappers supported by volunteers in many parts of the polecat's range. In sparsely populated areas, however, difficulties in achieving the target density will arise because trappers need to live close enough to sample squares to check traps over seven consecutive mornings.

6.4.1.3 The volunteer role

The contribution of volunteers to this live-trapping exercise was vital to its success. The deployment, through volunteers, of several sets of 16 live-traps by one full-time professional co-ordinator was the most efficient way of maximising the number of squares sampled. By this means it was just feasible to exceed a target of 50 1km squares sampled in one six-month trapping season. However, in future volunteer-based sampling exercises, two important considerations should be taken into account: the scale of demands placed upon volunteers, and the implications of the low capture rate of polecats in many areas.

Compared with other volunteer-based wildlife monitoring exercises, the VWT system is relatively demanding of time and effort. The need to check traps over seven consecutive mornings, taking approximately 1-3 hours each morning, means that it clearly cannot be conducted on a weekend-only basis in the way that British Trust for Ornithology (BTO) bird surveys and national badger and hare surveys can. Nor, for the same reasons, can sample squares be located too far from volunteers' homes. For example, whilst volunteers for the national hare survey by Hutchings and Harris (1996) were offered sample squares within a 50km radius of their homes, the majority of sample squares used for polecat-trapping were within 10km of volunteers' homes because of the need for several successive early morning visits. As a result of these constraints, many potential volunteers were understandably deterred from taking part because of conflicts with family and work commitments. Hence the distribution of volunteers influenced the location of sample squares considerably.

The low encounter rate with the target animal is an important consideration among volunteers expected to check traps throughout a 1km square on seven consecutive mornings during winter weather. Although the overall occurrence of positive squares, at 48.5%, compares favourably with the national hare survey (hares were seen in 38.2% of squares surveyed, Hutchings & Harris, 1996), the effort involved in terms of survey duration and distance covered is considerably greater in the polecat sampling exercise. Despite the commendable realism apparent in the attitude of volunteers, many who completed 'blank' squares were understandably disappointed not to have trapped a polecat as a reward for their efforts. The probability of encountering polecats through the VWT sampling exercise is especially low towards the fringes of the species' range, where fewer than one in three squares was positive. This has serious implications for the morale of volunteers, and Birks (1997) has suggested that there are parts of the polecat's range where trapping success is predictably so low that it would be unreasonable to involve volunteers.

6.4.2 Recommendations for future monitoring

Macdonald *et al.* (1998) make recommendations to Government for future monitoring of polecats in Britain based upon the live-trapping system developed by the VWT in this study. They suggest "a complete survey once per seven-year survey cycle, followed by sub-sample survey after a three year interval. In addition, annual surveys at the wavefront would be desirable". They suggest that full-time trappers, each running a series of two 1km sample squares simultaneously, could cover about 50 1km squares each per year on the October to March trapping 'window' basis. They recommend sampling a minimum of 500 1km squares every five years, with sites concentrated in Wales and England, "within and ahead of the polecat's expanding range". Notably, they suggest that sampling should include a 50km buffer zone around the limits of the polecat's known range where, given the findings of the present study, the likelihood of encountering the species by live-trapping would be very low indeed.

These suggested trapping targets are ambitious and need careful consideration. The proposed minimum of 500 1km squares is probably achievable with a co-ordinated deployment of a combination of professional trappers and substantial volunteer support. However, the commitment to repeat such a major exercise every five years may be difficult to justify in terms of the data it would generate. The VWT suggests a time interval of ten years (see Section 9.2.9).

Macdonald *et al.*, (1998) suggest using additional monitoring data from the GCT's National Game Bag Census. However, the doubtful legality of current lethal trapping of polecats by gamekeepers (Packer & Birks, 1999) and the possibility of future changes in trapping practice, notably in response to EU trapping protocols (M. Swan, pers. comm.), might make this source unreliable. Macdonald *et al.*, (1998) also recognise the importance of continued monitoring of changes in polecat distribution through roadkill data.

6.4.3 The influence of rabbits and main roads

Considering the quantitative limitations of the trapping data, the evidence of relationships with two variables of presumed biological significance to polecats, rabbit abundance and main road density, is encouraging. The positive association between polecats and the index of rabbit abundance in sample squares concurs with other evidence from this study of a strong predator-prey relationship between these species (see Section 8.3.8). Why this association should be apparent in the 'current core' of the polecat's range yet not in the 'fringe' is not clear. An explanation may lie in the greater apparent patchiness of polecat populations in the 'current fringe' vice-counties indicated by this study. Whilst polecats in the 'current fringe' were apparently at least as abundant as in the 'current core' wherever they occurred, they were unrecorded in proportionately many more squares. Thus, in parts of the 'current fringe' where rabbits are common, the high incidence of negative polecat sampling squares is likely to mask any association between the two species.

One possible source of the patchiness of polecat populations is suggested by the influence of variations in road density upon the numbers of polecats and the proportion of positive squares. Significantly, the inverse associations between road density and these variables were only apparent in the 'current fringe' of the species' range, where road and traffic densities are generally higher than in most of the 'current core' (see Figure 6.12; DETR, unpublished data; DETR, 1997).

The polecat is known to be especially vulnerable to road traffic (see Section 5.3.2.1). The results of this study suggest that mortality from this cause might lead to quite widespread population effects, to the extent that high traffic densities could conceivably limit the establishment of populations in some areas. This effect is currently the most probable explanation for the continuing absence of polecats from several 10km squares in the south Wales valleys (see Figures 5.7 and 6.12), where the density of main roads is high and, moreover, the roads tend to follow valley bottoms where polecat activity is most likely to be concentrated. A similar effect has been proposed as an explanation for the reduced density of badger setts near busy roads in Essex (Skinner *et al.*, 1991).

Whilst the influence of main roads as barriers to small mammals can be demonstrated (Richardson *et al.*, 1997), it is more difficult to confirm such effects on wide-ranging carnivores. An analysis of the effects of roads as dispersal barriers and causes of mortality in badgers in Britain suggests that these effects are significant and increasing (Clarke *et al.*, 1998). Their influence upon the dispersal and viability of polecat populations warrants further investigation. The results of the VWT study suggest that Britain's road network might be a significant factor in determining the pattern of future re-establishment of the polecat.

Areas of high traffic density might act as population sinks and as significant barriers to dispersal. Figure 6.12 indicates that there are many areas where main road densities are comparable with those in the south Wales valleys. The industrial north-west of England between Birkenhead and Leeds, the English West Midlands conurbation, parts of the East Midlands and Greater London and, to a greater or lesser extent their respective fringes, appear as predictably inhospitable terrain for polecats on the basis of main road density. Significant road casualty effects might also occur in rural areas where agricultural intensification and hedgerow removal result in the concentration of polecat activity in the relatively prey-rich habitats immediately adjacent to main roads.

6.4.4 A population estimate for the polecat in Britain in 1997

The data on polecat abundance and distribution from this live-trapping study and the distribution survey described in Section 5 can be used to produce a new population estimate for the polecat. There are many problems associated with estimating populations for British mammals. These are considered by Harris *et al.* (1995), who reviewed previous population estimates for the polecat based upon recorded distribution and on population densities from radio-tracking studies and gamekeeping records. On the basis of these density figures scaled up to the number of 10km squares in which the species was recorded, they estimated the minimum (ie. pre-breeding) British population to be 15,000 (12,500 in Wales and 2,500 in England). Though Harris *et al.*, (1995) recognised that reintroduced polecats might occur in Scotland, no estimate of their numbers was given. The authors acknowledged that this population estimate was only moderately reliable, with improvements likely to result in a change of up to 50% in the estimate.

Figure 6.12. Areas of high main road density in mainland Britain. The green areas indicate blocks of two or more contiguous 10km squares in which the length of 'A' roads exceeds 40km per 10km square. Vice-county boundaries are shown.

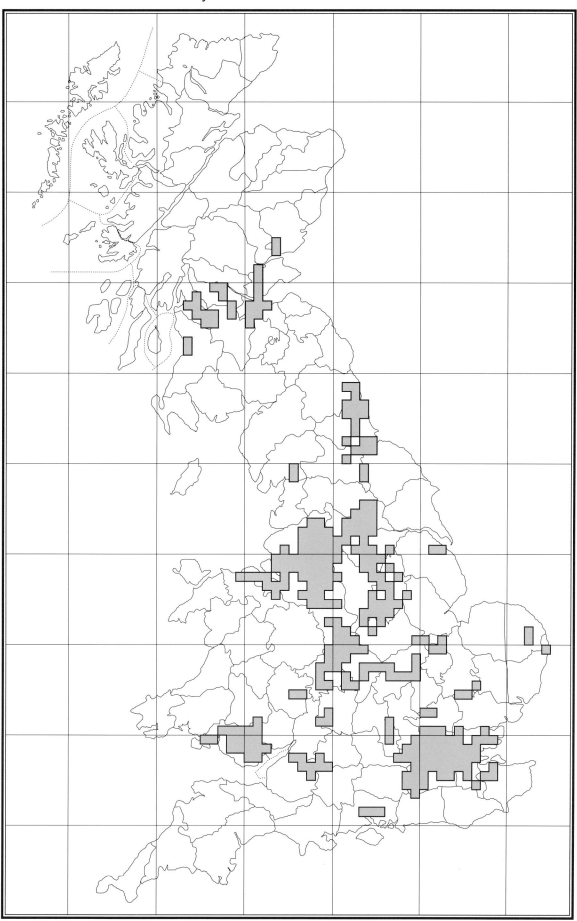

Because the VWT distribution survey has led to a near-doubling of the recorded range of the polecat (see Section 5.3.4), a new population estimate is likely to be much greater than the 15,000 estimated by Harris *et al.* (1995). Live-trapping data from the VWT study were used to derive two population density figures. Within the 'current core' of the polecat's range, defined in Figure 6.8, a mean density of 1.01 individuals per 1km square was recorded over all squares trapped. Outside this area in the 'current fringe' the figure was 0.69 individuals. These figures are within the range applied in previous population estimates (K. Walton and N. Teall, both quoted in Harris *et al.* (1995)). Applying these figures respectively to the number of 10km squares within the 'current core' (234 squares) and 'current fringe' (239 squares) of the polecat's range produces a minimum estimate of 38,381 for the whole British population, of which 22,270 are in the 'current core' and 16,111 are in the 'current fringe' (N.B. because 27 10km squares in the 'current core' and 11 squares in the 'current fringe' include substantial areas of sea, the estimated number of polecats per square is halved in these squares). The same approach is used to calculate separate population estimates for Scotland, Wales and England (see Table 6.8).

Table 6.8. A minimum population estimate for the polecat in Britain, based upon two mean population densities across the 473 10km squares recorded as occupied in 1997.

	Number of 'current core' 10km squares at 101 polecats per square	Number of 'current fringe' 10km squares at 69 polecats per square	Minimum population estimate
Scotland	0	6 (+2 at 50%)	483
Wales	134 (+27 at 50%)	36 (+9 at 50%)	17,691
England	73	186	20,207
Total	207 (+27 at 50%)	228 (+11 at 50%)	38,381

This population estimate must still be regarded as very approximate, not least because the density figures are derived from a sampling system which might underestimate the number of individuals. However, it is certainly based upon a more accurate distribution map than previously, which largely explains the considerable increase upon the earlier (but recent) estimate of 15,000 polecats. Significantly, this new estimate suggests that the polecat population of England is approximately 2,500 (14.2%) greater than that of Wales.

6.5 Acknowledgements

We are indebted to the many volunteers who cheerfully took on the sizeable task of running one or more sample squares. We thank Ian and Dilys Hart, Sue Holland, Mike Bailey, Ros and Anne Willder, John Davies, Ian Tillotson, Joan Daniels and colleagues, Bob Daniels and colleagues, Felicity Burge, Craig Stenson, Trevor Robinson, John Robinson, Mike Taylor, Andrew Lucas, Neil Matthews, Liz Flood, Tom Wall, Brian Chanin, Rob Macklin, Colin Fountain, Dave Evason, John Knowlson, John Webster, Tim McGrath, Phil Williams, Mike Howe, John Meiklejohn and friends, Stuart Corbett, Keith Mason, John Dutton, Ian and Phillipa McMurdo, Peter Murphy and colleagues, John and Norma Stevens, Jenny Grant, Susan Eaton, Dai Jarmon, Bob Haycock, Hugh Maw, John Messenger, John

Evans, Chris Bradley, Andrew Baines, Rob Colley and colleagues, Phil Richardson, Conor Kelleher, Trevor Trueman, Dan Burlingham, Jan and Keith Crowden, Tamlin Watson, Terry Smith, John and Shirley Martin, Steve Hewitt, Peter Lurz, Bernard Gillespie, Wolfgang Schaefer, Sylvia Ryman, Pam Blaxland, Dennis Howard, Jane Kelsall, Sheelagh Kerry, Peter Smith, James Hanlon, Annie and Martin Garnett, Martin Bailey, Mike Castle, Caroline Wilson, Julian Thompson, Anne Mynott, Richard Knight, Yvonne Parsett, Gordon Murray, Melvin Grey, Lin Gander, Tony Braithwaite, Michelle Bromley, Iolo Lloyd, Bill Evans, John Mackintosh, David Morris, Richard Austin, Tony Cooper, Bob Dennison, Adrian Turner, Sue Tatman, Shirley Reid, John Hainsworth, Keith Davies, Vera and Stuart Howard, Cliff Benson, Becky Palmer, Dave Hatfield, Frances Cattanach, Peter Brock, Julia Sheehan, Ian Thompson, Simon Young, Roger Matthews, Nigel McDonald, John Mitchell, Dave Hargreaves, Jack Grasse, Peter Walters Davies, John Street, Dave Wright, Jan King, Richard Farmer, Elinor Gwynn, Ian Langmead, Bryan Jones, Moira Convery, Terence Lambert, Richard Crompton, Barry Penney, M. and A. Thompson, Gareth Jones, John Swift, Verena Higgs, Jim Marshall, Mark Shannon, Shane Bates, Fiona Gale, Eamonn and Lynn Ritchie, Richard Eckton, Linda Barnett and Craig Emms.

We thank all landowners who granted permission for live-trapping to be carried out on their land. Special thanks are due to the owners and staff of Eastnor Castle Estate, and Mr. Gladwin of Hill Farm, Ledbury.

Mary Gough of the Centre for Land Use and Water Resources Research, University of Newcastle, kindly provided the data for Figure 6.12.

7. INTERACTIONS BETWEEN POLECATS AND FERRETS IN BRITAIN

A.C. Kitchener, J.D.S. Birks and A. Davison

7.1 Introduction

In recent years naturalists have often found great difficulty in distinguishing between polecats and feral ferrets, and even other mustelids such as the mink. In part, this is due to a lack of familiarity caused by the polecat's absence for several human generations in most parts of Britain, but there is also a real confusion about just what is a polecat or a ferret. For example, in Shetland feral ferrets are commonly referred to as 'polecats' and everywhere the term 'polecat-ferret' is variously defined as a polecat, a ferret or a hybrid between the two. This confusion has hampered efforts to record the true status and distribution of the polecat in Britain (see Section 5). Furthermore, the likelihood of hybridisation between polecats and feral ferrets has led to concerns about the present and future genetic integrity of the wild polecat. Therefore, there is a need to clarify the relationship between the two taxa and to identify any nature conservation consequences that might arise from their interactions.

7.2 Polecat systematics

The systematics or taxonomy of polecats and ferrets has long been uncertain. Some authors treat the ferret as a domesticated form or even a sub species of the western polecat, *Mustela putorius* (eg. Ellerman & Morrison-Scott, 1951; Rempe, 1970; Kruska, 1988), while others treat the ferret as a discrete species, *M. furo*, while recognising its polecat ancestry (eg. Clutton-Brock, 1981; Blandford, 1987; Blandford & Walton, 1991 a & b). Miller (1912; 1933) added further confusion to this debate by suggesting that because of a similar narrow post-orbital constriction and other cranial characters (see Figure 7.1), it was possible that the eastern or steppe polecat, *M. eversmannii*, could be the ancestor of the domestic ferret. This debate has raged until today (Blandford, 1987; Blandford & Walton, 1991 a & b), although Pocock (1932) demonstrated that the position and form of the post-orbital constriction was different in the two taxa, thus reinstating the western polecat as the ferret's only ancestor. The narrow post-orbital constriction of the ferret probably reflects the lesser development of the jaw musculature in captivity. The close relationship between the ferret and the western polecat is strongly supported by recent morphological, chromosomal and molecular studies (Rempe, 1970; Volobuev *et al.*, 1974; Davison *et al.*, 1998).

Figure 7.1. Dorsal views of skulls of western polecat (left), domestic ferret (centre) and steppe polecat (right) to show differences in shapes of post-orbital constrictions and nasal bones (after Miller, 1912; Pitt, 1921; Wolsan, 1993).

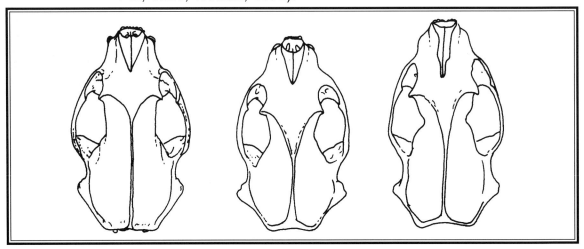

There has been further uncertainty regarding the status of the western and steppe polecats: some authors treat them as sub species of the same species, *M. putorius* (eg. Ellerman & Morrison-Scott, 1951), while most recent authors uphold their specific distinctness (eg. Heptner, 1964; Corbet, 1978; Blandford & Walton, 1991 a & b), which is supported by distinct cranial, behavioural and ecological differences between these two taxa (Heptner, 1964; Wolsan, 1993).

7.3 Ferrets

The polecat was first thought to have been domesticated more than 2,000 years ago probably somewhere in the Mediterranean region. The first mention of the ferret was by Aristotle in the 4th century B.C. (Thomson, 1951; Clutton-Brock, 1981; Owen, 1984). Ferrets were kept (as they are today) for bolting rabbits from their burrows and for controlling rodents (Clutton-Brock, 1981; Owen, 1984). Since bolting the quarry from burrows rather than killing it underground is the principal aim of ferreting (McKay, 1995), the process of domestication has involved selection against those predatory skills which might enable ferrets to catch the quarry underground. As a result there are significant behavioural differences between polecats and ferrets (Pitt, 1921; Poole, 1972; Blandford, 1987). This behavioural product of historical selective pressures may be of great significance in determining the outcome of the relationship between polecats and feral ferrets in the wild. Ferrets are usually considered to be albinos with white or cream-coloured fur and pink eyes. It has been suggested that albinos were deliberately selected by ferreters because they tended to be more docile and easy to handle (Porter & Brown, 1997), qualities which, together with their yellow-white fur, must seriously limit their ability to survive in the wild. However, ferrets with darker markings characteristic of the polecat to varying lesser degrees are called polecat-ferrets and these are extremely common in the captive population. Ferret-breeders have often hybridised ferrets with polecats to improve the bloodlines of domestic stock (Porter & Brown, 1997) and to increase the aggressiveness of their ferrets for rabbiting (McKay, 1995). Nowadays, it is said that the main incentive for ferret-breeders crossing their stock with polecats is to increase their chances of winning the 'polecat' class at ferret shows (S. Martin, Staffordshire Ferret Welfare, pers. comm.).

Plate 9. *Judging at Morecambe Ferret Show, October 1996. The true ferret is an albino animal with pink eyes (foreground); however, many ferret-keepers now favour the darker polecat-ferret (background).*

In Britain today ferret-keeping is a very popular activity. Ferrets are kept as working animals for bolting rabbits, as pets and as show animals (McKay, 1995; Porter & Brown, 1997). Concerns about traditional patterns of ferret-keeping have led to the establishment of an active ferret welfare movement, promoted through such organisations as the National Ferret Welfare Society (NFWS). This society seeks to improve the diet and living conditions of ferrets in captivity. It also promotes alternatives to the established wisdom that female ferrets must be bred from every year in order to maintain their health, such as mating with vasectomised males. Despite encouraging improvements in ferret husbandry, a surplus of young animals is produced each year, many of which are turned loose or disposed of in other ways (NFWS newsletter). The NFWS provides a rescue service for such animals and some centres receive between 50-100 ferrets per year (B. Witherstone, pers. comm.).

Plate 10. *Andrew Baines with polecat-ferrets at the National Ferret Welfare Society Christmas Show, Birmingham, December 1996. Apart from their tameness, unusually dark animals like the young male on the left may be indistinguishable from wild polecats.*

A potential problem for wild ancestors of domesticated species is that wherever the domesticate becomes feral within the indigenous wild species' range, there is the possibility of hybridisation. This has occurred in several species pairs, eg. wildcat and domestic cat (Kitchener, 1995; 1998); wolf and husky dog (Clutton-Brock *et al.* 1994); red deer and sika deer (Abernethy, 1994). Introgression of ferret genes into the wild polecat population could disrupt the co-adapted gene complexes, which have evolved within that species promoting its survival in its particular native environment and, thus, could compromise the survival of the species. Introgression also leads to increased morphological variation and this can affect the legal protection for the native species because it can no longer be easily identified and defined. This has already occurred in the case of the wildcat in Scotland (Kitchener, 1995, 1998; Balharry & Daniels, 1997).

Given the long history of ferret-keeping in Britain it might be suggested that the recovery of the polecat during the late 20th century is only an apparent recovery. Could the new populations have become re-established mainly through the escape of ferrets used for rabbit hunting? Or might re-colonising polecats have hybridised to varying degrees with feral ferrets when population densities were low, or where there was a lack of females due to greater dispersal of male polecats? Answers were needed to these questions in order to clarify the status of the polecat in Britain in the late 20th century.

7.4 Methods

A total of 465 polecat and feral ferret specimens was available for study. Most were prepared as skins, skulls and partial skeletons from road casualties and legal culls from throughout Britain. However, owing to crushing of skulls on the road and decay of specimens after death, it was not possible to prepare a skin and skeleton for each specimen. This study was greatly enhanced by the donation of a large collection of Welsh polecat skins and skulls by Walton, which he collected during his studies during the 1960s and 1970s. This important sample provided a baseline against which to compare variation in pelages and skulls from elsewhere in Britain. A small number of skins and skulls were loaned by private individuals and museums, eg. Tullie House Museum, Carlisle. Data were collected on pelage characters, skull measurements and skull characters. However, only the pelage characters and two skull measurements have been analysed so far, so that only the methodology appropriate to these is presented here in detail. Data from a separate study using mitochondrial DNA sequencing are summarised here, but full results are presented in Davison *et al.* (1998).

7.4.1 Pelage characters

A total of 286 skins was available for study. The skin of each preserved animal was scored for ten characters (see Table 7.1). Characters were chosen either from those given by different authors for discriminating polecats and ferrets (eg. Pitt, 1921; Pocock, 1932; Ashton, 1955; Ashton & Thompson, 1955; Blandford, 1987) or from visual inspection of skins of known taxonomic status. This was aided by a small series of skins which were from known polecat x ferret hybrids bred in captivity. Each character was given a score ranging from one for albino coloration to three for the darkest coloration. In other words, polecat character states were given the highest scores corresponding mainly to the darkest coloration and ferret character states were given the lowest scores corresponding to the palest coloration. Character states which were common to all ferrets and polecats were excluded from the scoring because they could offer no discrimination. In addition, the length of the pale throat patch displayed a bimodal frequency distribution (see Figure 7.2). Known hybrids and feral ferrets frequently had long throat patches, which were absent from Welsh polecats. Therefore, this character was recorded as a polecat character if less than 60mm long or as a ferret character if greater than or equal to 60mm long.

Table 7.1. Pelage characters that were scored for all polecat and ferret skins.

1.	Presence/absence of dark fur extending to nose
2.	Presence/absence of pale cheek patches or frontal band
3.	Coloration of paws
4.	Coloration of underfur on body
5.	Coloration of underfur on tail and limbs
6.	Presence/absence of scattered white hairs over body
7.	Coloration of dorsal surface of body
8.	Coloration of ventral surface of body
9.	Coloration of limbs
10.	Coloration of tail

For each skin or pelage the scores for each character were summed to give a pelage character total (PCT). In theory a polecat should have a PCT of (10 characters x 3) 30 and a ferret should have a PCT of (10 x 1) 10. Therefore, it should be possible to discriminate

Figure 7.2. Frequency distribution of throat patch lengths (TPLs) of polecats and ferrets.

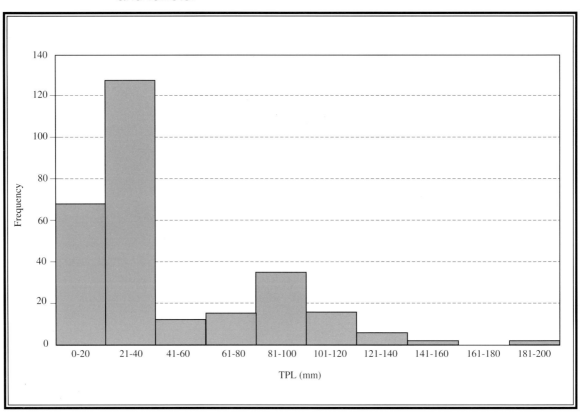

easily between these two mustelids. Scoring of characters was clearly subjective, so that two checks on the consistency of the scorer were made. Firstly, scores were made on pelages before the locality was recorded and compared with those where locality was known in advance, but this did not bias the scoring. Secondly, skins were re-scored several days later, but no difference was found between scores.

Polecats moult twice a year, in April/May and again in October/November (M. Clark, pers. comm.). Therefore, a comparison was made between PCTs of polecats and ferrets from the summer (April-September) and winter (October-March) to see if annual moults affected PCTs significantly. Correlation between the length of the throat patch and PCT was also examined to see if this could be used as a rapid means of distinguishing polecats and ferrets.

7.4.2 Skull measurements

A total of 307 skulls was available for study. Only the skulls of adults were used in this study, because juveniles have different skull shapes which could affect the interpretation of the results from multivariate morphometric studies. Juveniles were identified by unclosed skull sutures, unerupted or partially erupted permanent dentition, a small or absent sagittal crest or a rough texture to the bone.

Linear skull measurements were taken using dial calipers to an accuracy of 0.05mm. Twenty skull measurements were selected mainly from Buchalczyk and Ruprecht (1977) (see Table 7.2 and Figure 7.3). Where possible all unilateral measurements were taken on the right hand side of the skull. Brain case volume was also recorded using lead shot of 1-2mm diameter, which was poured into each skull until level with the foramen magnum. It was then poured into a $10cm^3$ measuring cylinder with $0.2cm^3$ gradations. Volumes in excess of $10cm^3$ were measured linearly within the cylinder using a ruler and converted to cm^3 based on the gradations.

Table 7.2. Skull measurements (and abbreviations) that were taken from all polecat and ferret skulls (see Figure 7.3).

1.	Condylobasal length (CBL)
2.	Palatal length (PL)
3	Zygomatic breadth (ZB)
4.	Ectorbital breadth (EOB)
5.	Frontal breadth (FB)
6.	Post-orbital breadth (POB)
7.	Length of waist (LW)
8.	Mastoid breadth (MB)
9.	Foramen magnum width (FMW)
10.	Foramen magnum height (FMH)
11.	Upper carnassial length (UP4L)
12.	Upper carnassial width (UP4W)
13.	Upper canine length (UCL)
14.	Upper canine width (UCW)
15.	Mandible length (ML)
16.	Mandible height (MH)
17.	Auditory bulla length (ABL)
18.	Auditory bulla width (ABW)
19.	Brain case height from bullae (BCH)
20.	Greatest length of skull (GLS)

To check for repeatability of measurements, six skulls were selected and measured six times for all 20 measurements. The percentage measurement error (ME%) was calculated using the within-individual coefficient of variation (Bailey & Byrnes, 1990; Lynch & Hayden, 1995):

$$ME\% = \frac{100(1+0.25.n)\,\sigma}{\bar{x}}$$

where n = sample size (ie. 6), σ = standard deviation, $\bar{x}$ = mean of the six replicates per specimen. Errors were mostly low, except for measurement 7 (length of waist) which

Figure 7.3. The measurements taken from the polecat and ferret skulls used in this study. The numbering of the measurements is as in Table 7.2.

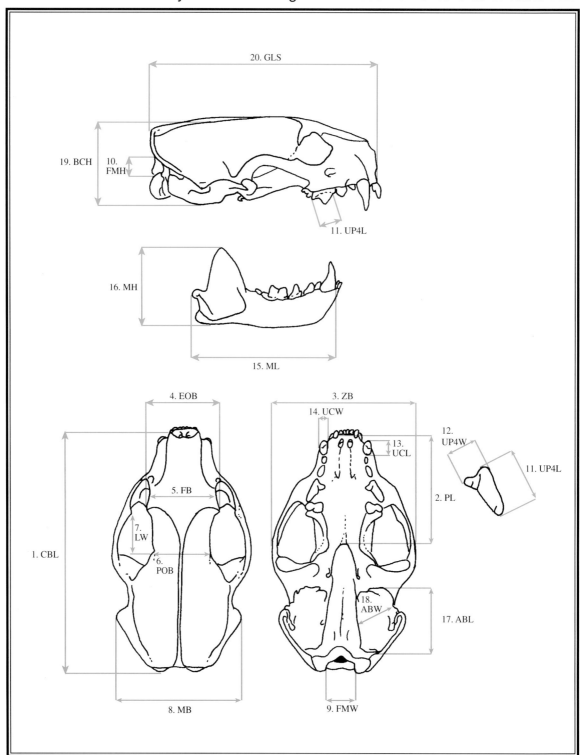

exceeded 2% and fell within the range of within-sex and population variation. Hence, this measurement was excluded from further analyses.

Two main skull measurements are analysed here, post-orbital breadth (POB) and cranial volume (CV). In the past, a POB of greater than or equal to 15mm was regarded as characteristic of a polecat, whereas ferrets had narrower POBs (Blandford, 1987; Blandford & Walton, 1991a). Also, domesticated mammals have characteristically lower CVs than their wild ancestors and this character has been used to discriminate between wild and feral forms of other species (eg. Schauenberg, 1969; Kruska, 1988; Hemmer, 1990). Both of these measurements were scaled against greatest skull length, which is known to be an accurate measure of overall body size (ACK pers. obs.).

7.4.3 Mitochondrial DNA sequencing

As its name suggests, mitochondrial DNA is found within the mitochondria of body cells rather than their nuclei. Mitochondria contain the enzymes that are mainly responsible for generating usable energy from food; ie. they are responsible for the basic metabolism. Compared with the hundreds of thousands of base pairs that make up the nuclear DNA of the chromosomes, mitochondrial DNA consists of a very short loop. This type of DNA has been well-studied, making it easier to look for mutational differences between species. Also, there are many mitochondria within each cell, so that it is relatively easy to extract large quantities of DNA for analysis.

Mitochondrial DNA is frequently used to determine relationships between species in systematic studies where species are presumed to be fairly closely related (eg. in the same genus). It is useful because it mutates rapidly (compared with most nuclear DNA), so that there are usually several differences in the sequence of base pairs of particular mitochondrial genes as a result of separation of the gene pools of these species since their origins from a common ancestor. It is assumed that the greater the number of base pair differences, the longer the time of separation between two taxa and hence the more distant the relationship between them.

In this study DNA was extracted from liver, blood or skin and hair specimens. The quantities of DNA fragments of three mitochondrial genes (cytochrome b, the control region or D loop, 12S rRNA) were greatly increased or amplified using the polymerase chain-reaction (PCR). Approximately 50ng of DNA was used to sequence the base pairs in both directions of each kind of fragment, including the relevant primer. For precise details of methods see Davison *et al.*, 1998.

Relationships between the differences in sequences of individual specimens were determined by constructing phylogenetic trees using various statistical programmes, including minimum evolution, maximum likelihood and maximum parsimony methods, which use different assumptions about the mutation rates that occur and the way in which a genetic distance is calculated.

7.5 Location of specimens

The skins and skulls of polecats and ferrets came from the following areas and were analysed as separate populations below:
1. Wales; indigenous polecats.
2. Herefordshire and Shropshire; indigenous/recolonised polecats.
3. Gloucestershire, Worcestershire, Staffordshire and Cheshire; recolonised polecats/feral ferrets.
4. Berkshire, Oxfordshire, Northamptonshire, Warwickshire and Derbyshire; recolonised/reintroduced? polecats/feral ferrets.
5. Cumbria and Yorkshire; reintroduced polecats/feral ferrets, plus some older indigenous polecats.
6. Argyll; reintroduced polecats/ferrets.
7. Sutherland; indigenous Scottish polecats (now extinct).
8. Scotland; feral ferrets/reintroduced polecats.
9. Scottish Islands; feral ferrets.
10. Captive; putative polecats reportedly derived from wild Welsh stock.
11. Isle of Man; feral ferrets.
12. South Uist, Western Isles (recent sample); feral ferrets (skulls only).
13. Shetland (recent sample); feral ferrets.

The specimens were grouped as above in order to provide meaningful comparisons between populations. There is potential for all mainland populations to be introgressed (interbred or hybridised) to varying degrees with feral ferrets and no museum specimens survive from before the arrival of the ferret in Britain (perhaps 1,000 years ago (Blandford, 1987)). Therefore, by comparing variation between populations with different origins and hence different potentials for introgression, it should be possible to establish which characters are most likely to distinguish between the two taxa. For example, Welsh animals are presumed to be pure polecats as are those from Herefordshire and Shropshire. In contrast, the island populations are known to be feral ferrets and have no possibility of hybridisation with polecats. Therefore, we can compare morphological variation in apparently recolonised English animals with that in indigenous polecats and feral ferrets.

7.6 Results

7.6.1 Pelage characters

7.6.1.1 Seasonal variation

Pelages from animals that died between April and September were classified as summer, whereas those from October to March were winter animals. The winter scores were significantly lower than summer scores ($t=2.016$ $df=127$, $p<0.025$). However, some pelage characters are unlikely to change from summer to winter (eg. character 1, see Table 7.1), so that the five characters most likely to change seasonally were analysed separately (extent of cheek patch (character 2), coloration of the underfur on body (4), tail and limbs (5) and the coloration of the dorsal (7) and ventral (8) surfaces of the body), which were also significantly different between summer and winter ($t=1.965$, $df=111$, $p<0.05$). However, the difference between the mean summer and winter PCTs was less than the range of variation within the Welsh polecat sample, so that summer and winter PCTs were combined for subsequent analyses of geographical variation.

7.6.1.2 Geographical variation

Figure 7.4a shows the relationship between PCT and throat patch length (TPL) of all specimens. There is clearly an inverse correlation between these two variables ($r=-0.473$, $df=100$, $p<0.0005$). Dark animals with mostly polecat characters have very short throat patches, whereas pale ferret-like animals have long throat patches. Nominal polecats are consistently high-scoring but they do not all score a maximum of 30 points. For example, Walton's Welsh polecats have PCTs that range from 23 to 30 points (see Table 7.3), excluding animals with throat patches $>=60$mm. The geographical samples (see Section 7.5) are significantly different for both PCT (ANOVA $F=16.195$, $df=8$, $p<0.001$) and TPL (ANOVA $F=15.948$, $df=8$, $p<0.001$). The differences between populations are described below.

Frequency distributions of PCTs show clear differences between populations. Welsh and Herefordshire populations are all high-scoring (see Figures 7.5 a,b and Table 7.3). Given that these areas have always been home to indigenous polecats, it is reasonable to assume that these populations remain mostly pure bred. Only 3.3% of Herefordshire/Shropshire and 2.2% of Welsh animals (including a recent sample) had ferret-like scores for PCT. The Sutherland polecats are also all high-scoring supporting their status as formerly indigenous polecats (see Figure 7.5c). Gloucestershire/Worcestershire etc. animals (population 3) are also mostly high-scoring, but there is a small proportion (13.5%) of lower-scoring individuals (to as low as 21) (see Figure 7.5d). The Berkshire/Oxfordshire etc. sample (population 4) is from further east and contains a higher proportion (24%) of lower-scoring animals (see Figure 7.5e). These populations represent putative recolonisations of indigenous polecats from the west, but the few low-scoring animals suggest some introgression with or presence of feral ferrets, the incidence of which increases eastwards. The Cumbrian polecats are slightly unusual: they comprise mostly fairly high-scoring animals (including some older, indigenous specimens from the late 19th and the first half of the 20th centuries), but there are also very low-scoring animals too (see Figure 7.5f). This polecat population was re-established through covert reintroductions in the 1970s and 1980s with allegedly pure Welsh polecats (see Section 5.3.5.5). Either these animals were not pure or there has been significant subsequent introgression with feral ferrets.

Figure 7.4a. The relationship between pelage character total (PCT) and TPL in polecats and ferrets.

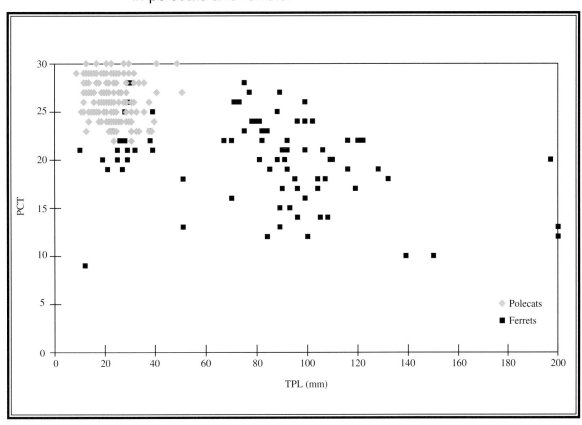

Figure 7.4b. The relationship between PCT and TPL in polecats and ferrets, including reintroduced animals from Argyll.

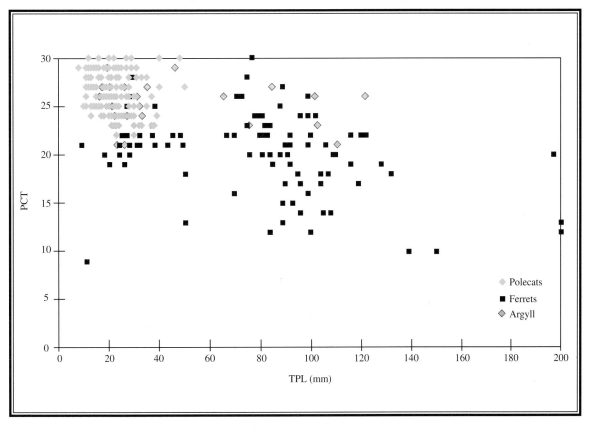

Figure 7.4c. The relationship between PCT and TPL in polecats and ferrets, including animals from the Isle of Man.

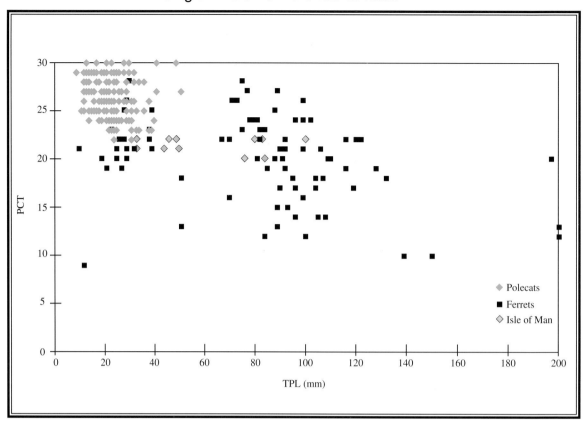

Figure 7.4d. The relationship between PCT and TPL in polecats and ferrets, including animals from Shetland.

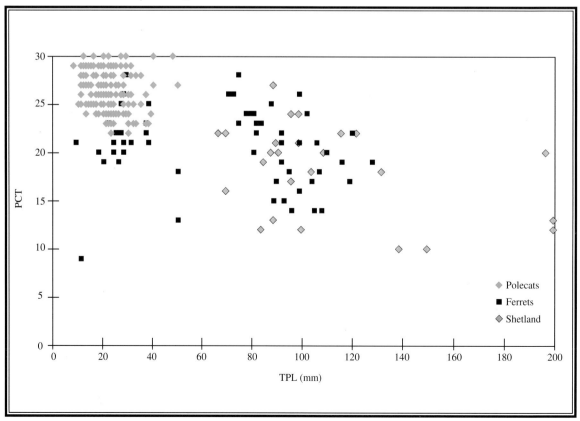

Table 7.3. Mean pelage character totals (PCTs) and throat patch lengths (TPLs) for polecats from different populations in Britain (*n*=sample size, S.D.=standard deviation).

Population	n	Mean PCT	S.D.	Mean TPL	S.D.	%PCT<23&TPL>=60mm
Wales	43*	26.63	1.90	20.42	6.23	0.00
	46	26.50	1.96	22.74	12.22	6.52
Herefordshire/ Shropshire	60	26.60	2.14	25.93	13.50	6.67
Glos./Worcs. etc.	37	25.51	2.29	28.35	18.70	13.51
Berks./Oxon. etc.	25	25.24	3.41	29.80	14.09	24.00
Cumbria/Yorks.	19	23.00	3.93	55.00	37.95	42.10**
Argyll	22	25.18	2.34	48.82	34.64	40.90
Sutherland	3	27.00	1.00	21.00	8.54	0.00
Scotland	9	19.67	6.00	64.33	35.18	77.78
Scottish Islands	16	18.94	5.03	88.31	44.07	87.50
Captive	9	19.11	3.79	92.12	40.54	100.00
Isle of Man	12	21.42	0.79	66.17	27.26	100.00
Shetland	26	17.96	4.81	91.62	43.56	100.00

* Standardised sample excluding specimens with PCT<23 and TPL>=60mm.
** Before 1950 25% ferret-like; after 1950 46.67% ferret-like.
N.B. The South Uist animals (population 12 in Section 7.5) are excluded from this analysis because only skulls were available.

Animals from mainland Scotland (see Figure 7.5c) and the Scottish Islands show a wide range of variation in PCT (Scottish mainland range 11-30; Scottish Islands range 6-27) showing that these are all feral ferrets. The recently reintroduced population in Argyll contains mostly animals with similar PCTs to those of Welsh polecats, although a significant proportion (13.6%) of lower-scoring individuals suggest subsequent introgression with feral ferrets which have been recorded there (see Figures 7.4b and 7.5g). A high proportion (31.8%) of Argyll animals also had long throat patches confirming the influence of ferrets within this population. This contrasts with animals from the Isle of Man, which although morphologically very similar to each other, were clearly all ferrets by the criteria developed here (see Figures 7.4c and 7.5g).

A large sample of animals was from Shetland as a result of a bounty scheme co-ordinated by Shetland Farming and Wildlife Advisory Group on behalf of Shetland Islands Council. These animals score consistently low PCTs and have long TPLs, which is consistent with their feral ferret origin (see Figures 7.4d and 7.5h). Despite being feral for at least a dozen generations (Johnston, 1999), there is no evidence of reversion to the wild type in pelage characteristics.

Across southern Britain there is a general decline in PCT from west to east (see Figure 7.6) which is suggestive of a recolonisation of central and eastern England with introgression with feral ferrets. This is not surprising because it would be expected that male polecats disperse further than females, so that males in new areas may have had no alternative but to mate with feral ferret females. It will be interesting to see whether this situation remains stable, or whether there is an increase in PCTs eastwards as colonising polecats consolidate in these areas.

95

Figure 7.5a. Frequency distribution of PCTs of polecats from Wales, excluding animals with throat patches >=60mm long.

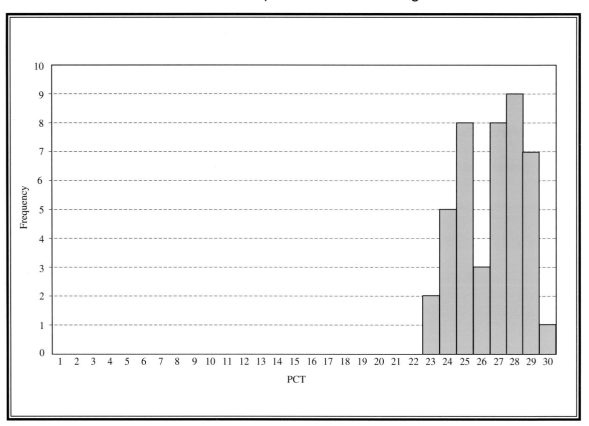

Figure 7.5b. Frequency distribution of PCTs of polecats from Herefordshire and Shropshire.

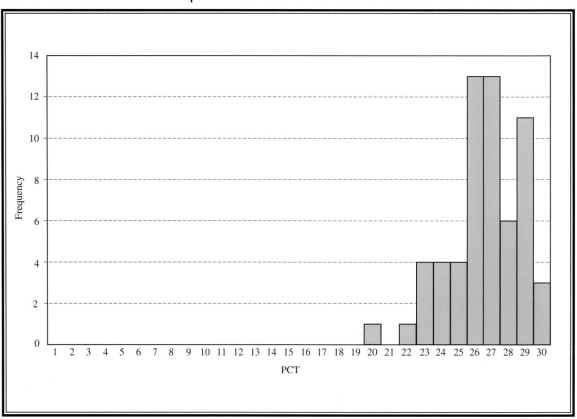

Figure 7.5c. Frequency distribution of PCTs of polecats from Sutherland and feral ferrets from Scotland.

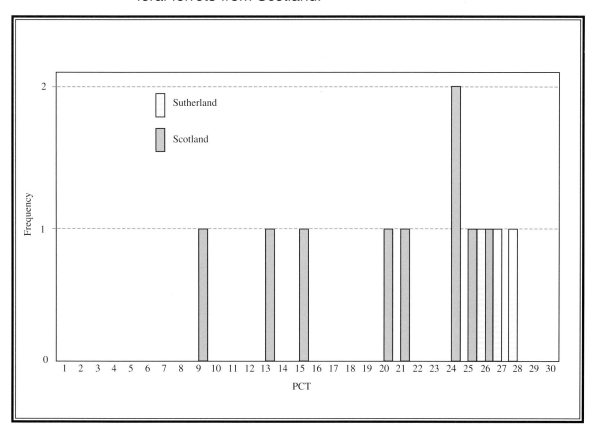

Figure 7.5d. Frequency distribution of PCTs of polecats from Gloucestershire, Worcestershire, Staffordshire and Cheshire.

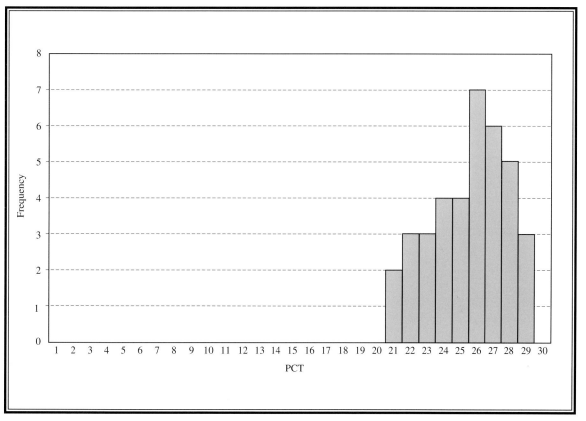

Figure 7.5e. Frequency distribution of PCTs of polecats from Berkshire, Oxfordshire, Northamptonshire, Warwickshire and Derbyshire.

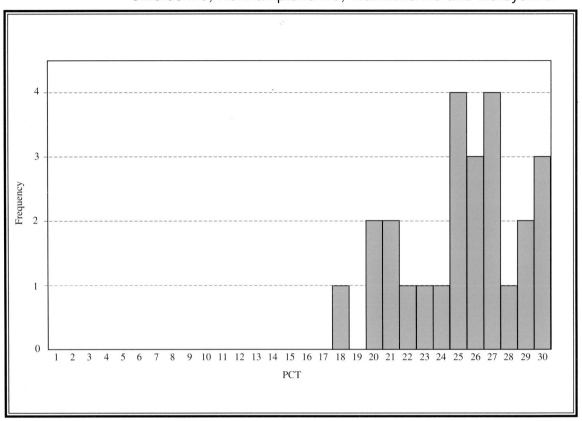

Figure 7.5f. Frequency distribution of PCTs of polecats from Cumbria and North Yorkshire.

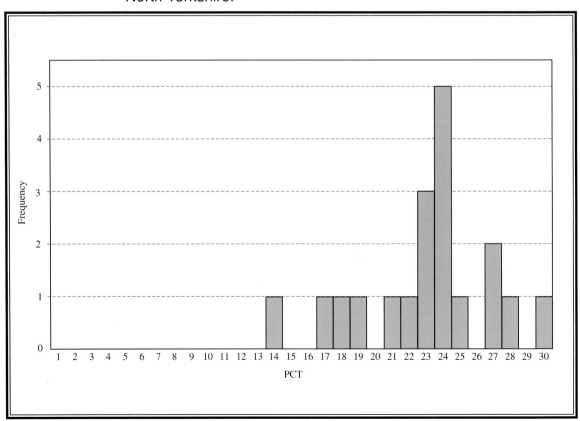

Figure 7.5g. Frequency distribution of PCTs of feral ferrets from the Isle of Man and reintroduced polecats from Argyll.

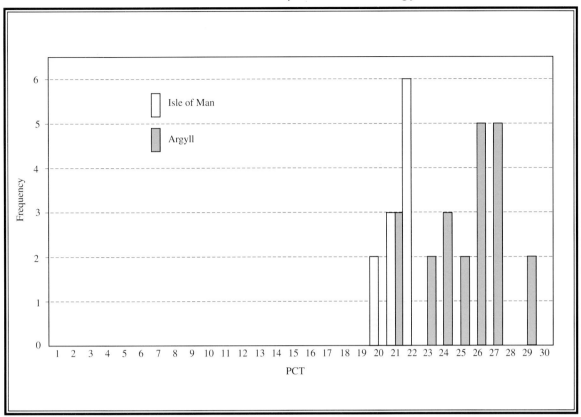

Figure 7.5h. Frequency distribution of PCTs of feral ferrets from Shetland.

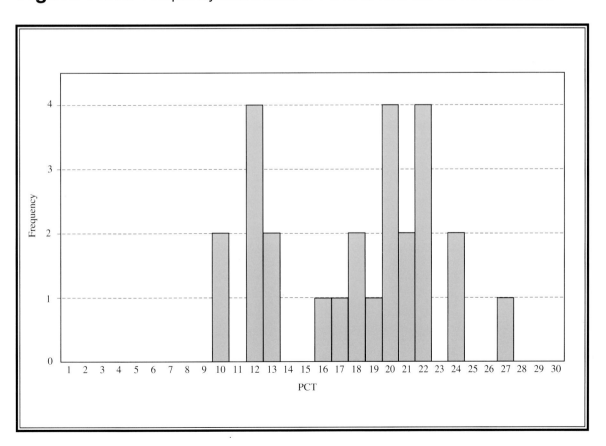

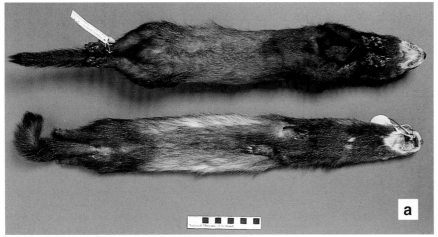

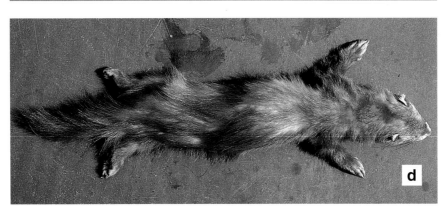

Plate 11.

Geographical variation in the pelage of British polecats and feral ferrets from the 1990s:

a) ventral view of Welsh polecat skins, showing range of variation in PCTs from 30 (above) to 23 (below)

b) ventral view of polecat skins, showing variation in throat patch length, from Cumbria (left) and Herefordshire (right) compared with known captive-bred polecat x ferret hybrids (centre)

c) dorsal view of ferret skins from Shetland, showing range of variation in PCTs

d) dorsal view of an erythristic polecat found as a road casualty near Little Faringdon, Oxfordshire in August 1997, showing replacement of the black guard hairs with red ones (note the white fur on the ear tips and muzzle, confirming this as a polecat rather than an oddly-coloured ferret).

(Photographs a, b and c from National Museums of Scotland.)

7.6.2 Skull measurements

In order to facilitate the interpretation of skull measurements, the data were divided into 'polecats' and 'ferrets'. Firstly, populations 1 to 4 and 7 were regarded as polecats and populations 8 to 12 were regarded as ferrets (see Section 7.5). Populations 5 and 6 were classified as polecats and ferrets according to their pelage characters (see below). However, this provides only a crude differentiation between forms (see Tables 7.4 and 7.5; total samples). Secondly, all skulls with an associated pelage from populations 1 to 7 were categorised as polecats on the basis of minimum PCTs of 23 and TPLs of <60mm. The remaining British animals were regarded as ferrets or ferret/polecat introgressive hybrids (see Tables 7.4 and 7.5 (pelage samples); Figure 7.4a)) (there is no way of or practical value in distinguishing between ferrets and hybrids by the criteria established here). Figure 7.7 shows the scaling of POB in male polecats and ferrets. Polecats have a consistently greater POB than ferrets of similar size, but there is some overlap with presumably introgressive hybrids. For example, Pitt (1921) showed that whereas F1 (first generation) hybrids from a mating between a male polecat and female albino ferret had pelages that were polecat-like, their crania were distinctly ferret-like. Subsequent backcrosses of these F1 hybrids to polecats (ie. introgressed hybrids) had polecat-like skulls and more ferret-like pelages. Most ferrets have a POB greater than 15mm so that this method cannot be used for discrimination between ferrets and polecats. Half the known Sutherland polecats (only *n*=2!) have a POB consistent with other polecats, as do many of the Cumbrian and Argyll animals. However, in both of these latter areas there are many animals with a low POB, suggesting a high proportion of ferrets and/or introgression with ferrets. The Isle of Man animals are consistently ferrets by this character.

There is clear sexual dimorphism in POB and the difference between polecats and ferrets is still evident (see Figure 7.8). The lower sample size for females from each area makes it difficult to draw firm conclusions, but patterns of variation are consistent with those of males.

CV is relatively less in male ferrets than male polecats (see Figure 7.9) as would be expected for a domesticate. The mean polecat CV is about 13% greater than the mean

Figure 7.6. Mean PCTs of polecat populations from west to east. The populations are from Wales (1), Herefordshire/Shropshire (2), Glos/Worcs etc. (3) and Berkshire/Oxon etc. (4). Bars show ± S.D.

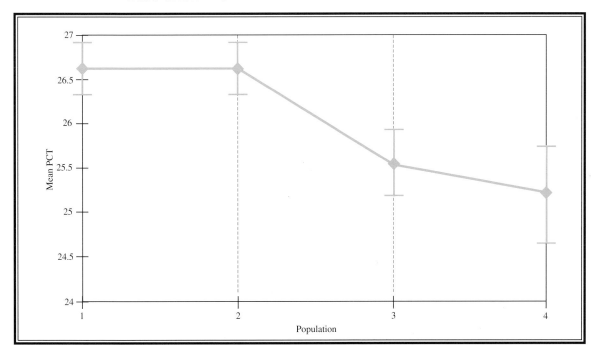

ferret's, which is less than that measured by Kruska (1988; c. 30% reduction), but the ferrets in this study were wild-living and would be expected to have a greater CV than laboratory animals (see also Hemmer, 1990; Lynch & Hayden, 1995; Kruska, 1996). However, there was some overlap between putative polecats and ferrets suggesting that this character cannot be used exclusively to distinguish between the two forms. In total, there is much less morphological difference between the skulls of polecats and ferrets than there is between those of wildcats and domestic cats (Schauenberg, 1969; Kitchener, 1998). There is also sexual dimorphism in CV with consistent, but not complete, differences between female polecats and ferrets (see Figure 7.10).

Table 7.4. Mean POBs of polecats and ferrets.

Sex/Form	n	mean POB (mm)	S.D.
Males			
Polecats (total sample)	90	16.38	1.34
Polecats (pelage sample)	46	16.56	0.84
Ferrets (total sample)	114	15.74	0.90
Ferrets (pelage sample)	46	15.68	0.99
Females			
Polecats (total sample)	44	15.52	1.04
Ferrets (total sample)	48	14.24	0.78

Table 7.5. Mean cranial volumes (CVs) of polecats and ferrets.

Sex/Form	n	mean CV (cm^3)	S.D.
Males			
Polecats (total sample)	92	10.15	0.92
Polecats (pelage sample)	45	10.17	1.05
Ferrets (total sample)	110	8.96	0.83
Ferrets (pelage sample)	43	9.01	0.62
Females			
Polecats (total sample)	39	8.34	0.68
Ferrets (total sample)	47	7.03	0.55

Figure 7.11 shows that there is a high degree of correlation between POB and CV in the skulls of male polecats and ferrets. Moreover, it provides a high degree of separation between polecats and ferrets, except for some smaller male polecats. This suggests that brain size rather than development of jaw musculature is the primary determinant of POB size.

Figure 7.7. The relationship between post-orbital breadth (POB) and greatest length of skull in male polecats and ferrets. The horizontal line shows the 15mm rule which was said to distinguish polecats from ferrets (see Section 7.6.2).

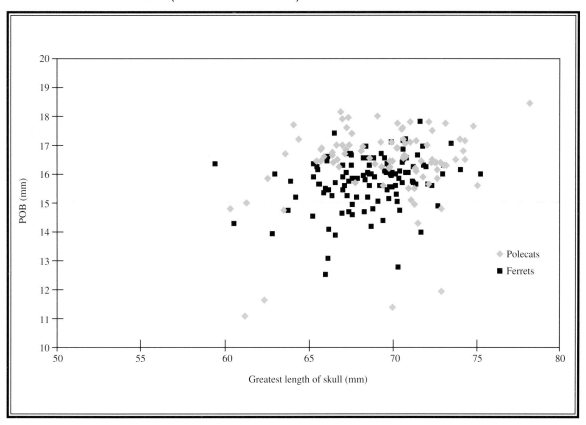

Figure 7.8. The relationship between POB and greatest length of skull in male and female polecats and ferrets.

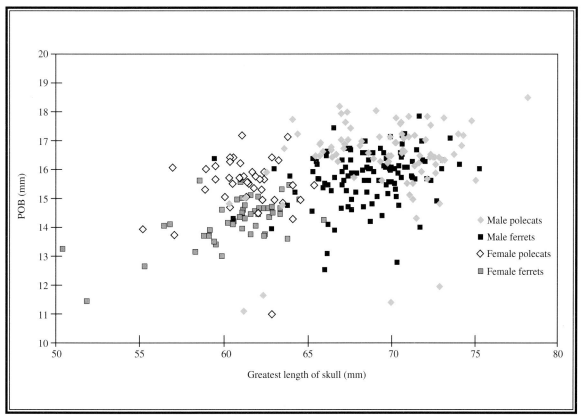

Figure 7.9. The relationship between cranial volume (CV) and greatest length of skull in male polecats and ferrets.

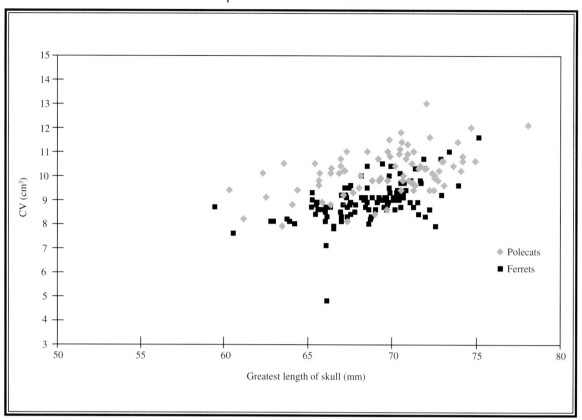

Figure 7.10. The relationship between CV and greatest length of skull in male and female polecats and ferrets.

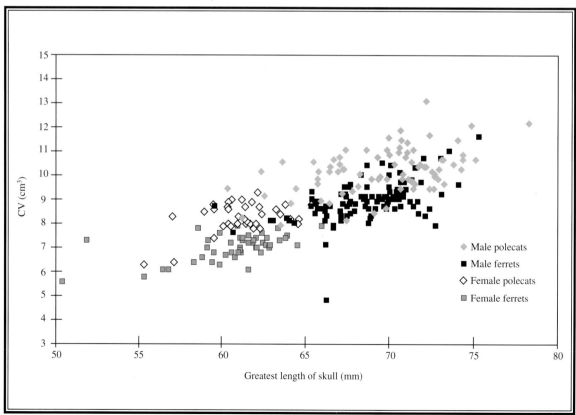

Figure 7.11. The relationship between CV and POB in male polecats and ferrets.

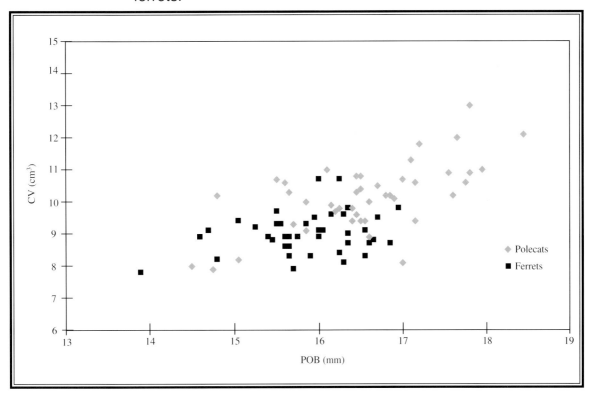

7.6.3 Mitochondrial DNA sequence variation between polecats and ferrets (summarised from Davison *et al.*, 1998)

Only two cytochrome b haplotypes or variants were discovered in all polecats and ferrets sampled. However, they differed by only a single base transition at a third codon position, so that genetic differences between polecats and ferrets are minimal. One haplotype was confined to the 'current core' of the polecat's range in Wales and western central England and is called the Welsh Polecat (WP) haplotype. The other haplotype was found widely in both polecat and feral ferret populations in mainland England, Wales and Scotland, and on islands including Benbecula, Shetland and the Isle of Man, and was identical to two domestic ferret cytochrome b sequences on the GeneBank database. It is called the Ferret (F) haplotype. Also, the two cytochrome b haplotypes corresponded to two distinct D-loop and 12S rRNA clades. Therefore, all morphologically 'good' polecats from the recolonised range in central and southern England and from reintroduced populations in Cumbria and Argyll had the F haplotype rather than the presumed ancestral WP haplotype of indigenous Welsh polecats.

7.6.4 Correlation of pelage and skull characters

If the pelage and skull characters identified here separately really do distinguish between putative polecats and ferrets, correlation between PCT, POB and CV would be expected. Figure 7.12a shows the relationship between PCT and POB in males. It is clear that there is a strong correlation between these two variables, but pelage characters provide most discrimination. CV is more strongly correlated with PCT (see Figure 7.12b), providing better discrimination between the two forms. Similar, although negative, correlations are seen between TPL and the two skull measurements (see Figures 7.12c and d). These results show that broad POBs, high CVs, high PCTs and short TPLs are all characteristic of polecats.

7.6.5 Erythristic polecats

Two erythristic polecats were found during the survey. One of each sex were recovered as road casualties from locations some 30km apart in Oxfordshire in 1997 (Little Faringdon

Figure 7.12a. The relationship between POB and PCT in male polecats and ferrets.

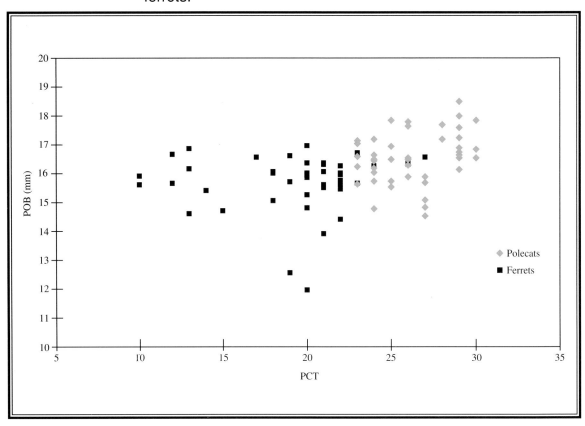

Figure 7.12b. The relationship between CV and PCT in male polecats and ferrets.

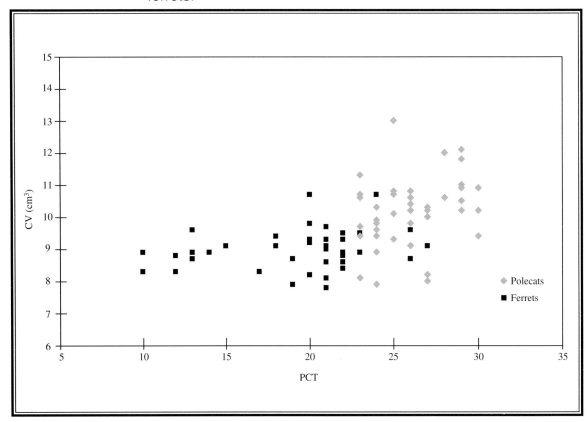

106

Figure 7.12c. The relationship between POB and TPL in male polecats and ferrets.

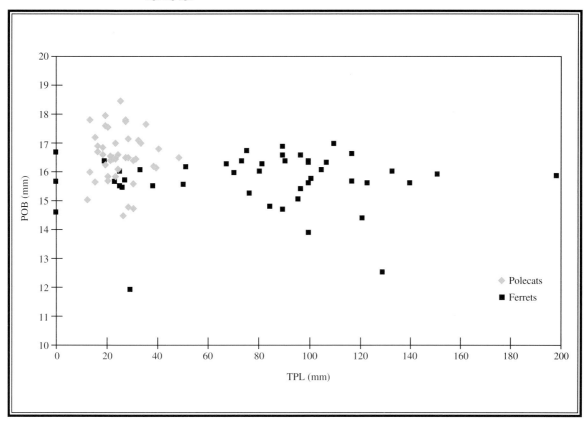

Figure 7.12d. The relationship between CV and TPL in male polecats and ferrets.

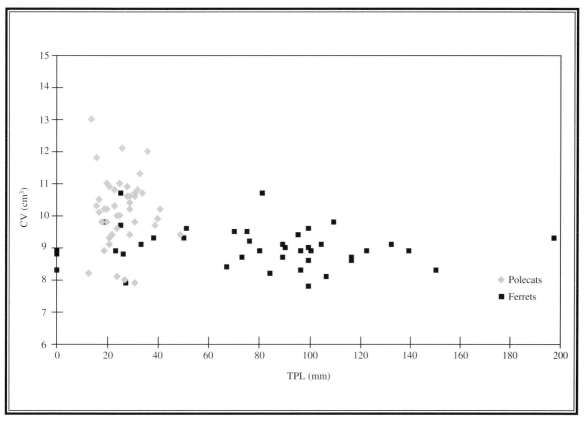

- see Plate 11d) and 1998 (Chipping Norton). Fragments of a further probable erythristic polecat, reported as a road casualty pine marten, were recovered from near Llandeilo in Carmarthenshire in 1995. During his research in the 1960s, Walton (1968a) encountered only one erythristic polecat, from Llandinam, Montgomeryshire in 1967.

7.7 Discussion

This preliminary study of polecat and ferret morphological discriminants confirms that there are significant differences in the pelage and skulls between these two forms. Pelage characteristics alone do provide a reliable method for distinguishing between individual live animals in the hand, but are unlikely to prove useful for sight identification in the field except at the extremes of variation. The darker pelage characters and short throat patches associated with polecats are also correlated with a wide POB and a greater CV, which allows for a more certain identification of dead animals, although there is some overlap in skull characteristics between putative polecats and ferrets.

Mitochondrial DNA sequencing by Davison *et al.* (1998) indicates that polecats and ferrets in Britain and Europe are genetically very similar. However, two distinct mitochondrial lineages exist in British polecats. One is centred on the polecat's core refugial range (the WP haplotype); the other (the F haplotype) occurs throughout Britain, and probably wherever there are (or have been) feral ferrets. It is most likely that these two haplotypes in Britain are derived from the ancestral polecat and the domestic ferret respectively. The wider geographical distribution of the polecat phenotype, compared with the matrilineal WP haplotype, is consistent with range expansion being mediated by dispersing male polecats occasionally breeding with feral ferrets. This is also consistent with Pitt's (1921) observations of the dominance of wild-type pelage characters over ferret pelage characters in F1 hybrids of male polecat x female ferret mating. Equally, this pattern might be expected to arise wherever there is strong selection for the polecat phenotype in populations dominated by the F haplotype.

Whilst it has provided complementary evidence for the distinction between the two main forms, mitochondrial DNA is not sufficiently discriminatory to categorise individual animals as polecats, ferrets or hybrids. This would require further studies using more sensitive microsatellite DNA fingerprinting techniques.

7.7.1 How do polecats and ferrets interact in the wild?

Excluding captive situations, opportunities for wild polecats to interact with ferrets are provided by the occurrence of viable feral ferret populations surviving in the wild and by the frequent loss or escape of captive ferrets into the wild. Ferrets might interact with wild polecats in two ways. Firstly, by acting as competitors for scarce resources such as food and shelter and secondly, by mating with polecats to produce hybrids. In assessing or predicting the influence which ferrets might have upon the conservation status of the polecat in Britain, it is important to understand the nature of these ecological and genetic interactions.

Relatively little is known about the occurrence and status of feral ferret populations in Britain. Blandford and Walton (1991b) identify the islands of Mull, Lewis, Bute, Arran and the Isle of Man 'as well as several places on the mainland' as supporting significant numbers of feral ferrets. They recognise that the widespread occurrence of recently escaped animals makes it difficult to detect well-established populations. The VWT survey has confirmed that feral ferret populations are also now well-established in mainland Shetland, South Uist in the Western Isles, parts of mainland Scotland (eg. Speyside and Sutherland) and possibly in the Yorkshire Dales. Despite the volume of ferrets lost into the wild each year (see Section 7.3), self-sustaining feral ferret populations are apparently scarce on the British mainland.

The greater prevalence of thriving feral ferret populations on offshore islands compared with the British mainland is significant. Considering the higher density of ferret-keepers in many mainland areas and consequently greater opportunities for establishing feral populations, the scarcity of such populations there may reflect the poor survival skills of ferrets. Typically, ferrets have been bred for docility, and to show low levels of movement, alertness and fear. In addition to limiting survival, these characteristics would be distinctly disadvantageous in any direct interaction between polecats and ferrets and may also explain why hybridisation has probably been mainly between male polecats and female feral ferrets. However, on offshore islands the scarcity or absence of competing carnivores and the resultant abundance of prey (typically rabbits) enable feral ferret populations to thrive more successfully than they are capable of doing on the mainland. In contrast, the wild polecat's current successful recovery on the mainland provides a pointer to how ecological competition between the two forms is likely to be resolved. The wild polecat phenotype is clearly out-performing its feral ferret counterpart, suggesting that domestication has severely limited the direct competitive threat which the feral ferret poses to wild polecats.

The apparent competitive advantage associated with the polecat phenotype permits optimistic predictions, in terms of polecat conservation, about the selective pressures acting upon individuals and populations containing both polecat and ferret genes. Those animals possessing and expressing ferret genes are likely to be at a disadvantage in competition with animals of the polecat phenotype. Therefore, in the absence of constant and significant contributions of escaped ferrets to populations, polecat genes should gradually predominate in successive generations at the expense of ferret genes.

The incidence of lost or escaped ferrets is difficult to determine, but is probably related to geographical variations in ferreting activity which, in turn, are influenced by variations in rabbit abundance. A questionnaire survey by Packer and Birks (1999) indicated that ferreting was more prevalent on farms in the English Midlands than in Wales, probably reflecting the greater abundance of rabbits on lowland farmland in central and eastern Britain (Trout *et al.*, 1986; Tapper, 1992). For example, in Norfolk the NFWS typically receives 50-100 unwanted or abandoned ferrets per year (B. Witherstone, pers. comm.).

The extent to which ferrets might hybridise with polecats in the wild is influenced by several factors. Since the main ferreting season is in mid-winter (Porter & Brown, 1997), this is when most ferrets are likely to be lost into the countryside. These animals must then survive in good condition until late March if they are to participate effectively in the mating season. Given the competitive disadvantages associated with the ferret phenotype, many escaped ferrets must fail to meet even this basic requirement, especially in those areas where wild polecats are well-established, so that as a result competition for resources is intense and few vacant territories are available. If feral ferrets survive until the mating season, the two sexes face severe and different pressures if hybridisation is to occur. Females must withstand the violent attentions of male polecats and must subsequently maintain a food intake sufficient to see them through the exceptionally demanding period of pregnancy, lactation and provisioning of prey for their growing offspring. Males must compete for access to females with wild male polecats which are likely to be stronger and more aggressive than themselves.

This analysis suggests that the most likely scenario for successful hybridisation is in areas where polecats are scarce and, hence, where ferrets face least competition for resources and mates. Hybridisation could also occur where polecats are recolonising an area because, typically, male polecats probably disperse more widely than females, so that most matings would occur between male polecats and female ferrets. The presence of the ferret haplotype in these recolonised populations with a polecat phenotype appears to confirm this scenario. These conditions are most likely to be met at the fringes of the polecat's range where its distribution is more patchy (see Section 6.3.3.2), or where small numbers of polecats are present as isolated populations, eg. in areas where the species has been recently reintroduced.

Stories of tame female ferrets recovered after becoming pregnant during a period in the wild occasionally come to light. One such animal, an albino, was recovered by the NFWS in the spring of 1997 near Tring in Hertfordshire where a small reintroduced population of wild polecats is now re-established. She subsequently gave birth to ten dark polecat-ferret hybrids which had some wild characteristics and proved difficult to handle (M. Neale, pers. comm.). It seems that this female had been mated by a wild male polecat.

7.7.2 Are there any true polecats in Britain?

On the basis of the morphological patterns observed in this study, it is confirmed that true polecats still occupy Wales, Herefordshire and Shropshire, and that they have subsequently recolonised a wide area of central England as far east as Northamptonshire and Oxfordshire. However, the proportion of ferret-like animals in each county sample increases towards the east, suggesting a dilution of the recolonisation by introgression with, or presence of, feral ferrets. However, it will be necessary to repeat sampling of the populations to see if, as predicted above, the recolonising polecats are able to overcome this diluting effect over time as they consolidate their current range.

Elsewhere in Britain isolated populations conform to their presumed origin. Cumbrian and Argyll populations are said to be derived from recent reintroductions of polecats of Welsh origin. Whilst the size of samples was relatively small, only the ferret haplotype was detected in these populations, suggesting either a hybrid origin and/or extensive introgression. The proportion of animals with a 'ferrety' phenotype is greater in Cumbria than in Argyll, perhaps reflecting the greater use of ferrets for rabbiting in Cumbria with the consequential escape of working ferrets. Anecdotal evidence indicates that a feral ferret population did exist in lowland east Cumbria at the time of the reintroduction of polecats there from the 1970s onwards. Whilst many polecat specimens recovered from this area appeared to be introgressive hybrids, such animals have apparently become scarcer in recent years, and the majority now conform to the polecat phenotype (S. Hewitt, pers. comm.). Despite the evidence of introgression, these isolated reintroduced polecat populations have some conservation value, and should not be regarded as merely feral ferrets. Sampling of road casualties should be continued in these populations in order to monitor the predicted advance of the polecat phenotype.

On both genetic and morphometric evidence the Isle of Man population is clearly made up of feral ferrets, as are the populations in Shetland, the Western Isles, Mull and the mainland of Scotland (excluding Argyll). On some islands with a long-recorded history of feral populations (notably Mull and the Isle of Man) there is no evidence of long-term selection for the polecat phenotype in populations clearly derived from ferret stock, contrary to perceived wisdom (eg. Pocock, 1932). However, in ecological terms all feral ferret populations probably fill a polecat niche. Given the lack of pure polecats in the original gene pools of these island introductions, it seems unlikely that natural selection acting on such populations even in the long-term could result in the polecat phenotype eventually reasserting itself in the absence of introgression with wild polecats. From this study it can be seen that all island ferrets are readily distinguishable from putative polecats on the basis of pelage and skull characters, including CV. Long-term monitoring of island ferret populations, where true polecats are absent and injections of domestic ferrets are limited, would provide a valuable experimental control for assessing the purity of recolonising polecat populations on the mainland.

7.8 Acknowledgements

We are most grateful to the Nigel Easterbee Memorial Fund for its generous support of the preparation of polecat and ferret specimens for this study. Many people collected road kills to send to us, notably Colin Fountain who donated the two erythristic polecats among many others to the National Museums of Scotland. We thank Ruth Pollitt and Phil Howard for skinning and sampling hundreds of animals, and Alan Lothian for preparing an equal number of skulls. We would like to thank Ken Walton for his generous donation of Welsh polecat skins and skulls to the National Museums of Scotland. We are grateful to Carl Jones for donating his skull collection too and Clive Craik for donating a series of specimens from Argyll and Wales. Loans of specimens were kindly made available to us by Paul Unwin (private collection) and Steve Hewitt of the Tullie House Museum, Carlisle. We are especially grateful to Vivienne Pratt for carrying out an initial pilot study on skulls and pelages, which forms the basis of this section, and to Chris Gall for continuing the study.

8. ECOLOGY OF THE POLECAT IN LOWLAND ENGLAND

J.D.S. Birks and A.C. Kitchener

8.1 Introduction

The polecat is one of the least-studied British mammals, with the result that its behaviour and ecology are still poorly understood. Prior to the VWT project, only two major studies of polecat field biology in Britain had been published. Walton (1968a) concentrated his MSc. study on basic biology, using a sample of corpses to examine pelage variation, morphology, reproductive biology, diet, population characteristics and parasite burdens. Following a pilot study near Llandrindod Wells by the Ministry of Agriculture, Fisheries & Food (MAFF) (Wilcox, 1978), Blandford (1986) undertook a field-based PhD. study of the behavioural ecology of the polecat in the same area of mid-Wales.

Unsurprisingly, these studies were based in the species' Welsh stronghold. However, the distinctive landscape there makes it difficult to extrapolate Welsh data on polecat behaviour to the fringes of the species' range. For example, the rugged, upland character of Blandford's (1986) mid-Wales study area differs very considerably from the intensively managed lowland landscapes now occupied by the polecat in parts of the English Midlands. In order to understand the polecat's current recovery and the factors which might influence it in future, there was a need to improve knowledge of polecat ecology on lowland farmland, a landscape which dominates the fringe of the species' current range. Therefore, the VWT survey included radio-tracking and dietary studies which are described in this section. These were designed to generate simple, descriptive information on home range, feeding ecology, habitat use and polecat interactions with rural enterprises. Polecat social organisation was not a priority for study, and was precluded on logistical grounds because of the need to radio-track several animals simultaneously.

A significant polecat conservation issue, accidental poisoning with anticoagulant rodenticides, was confirmed during the radio-tracking work. This necessitated a specific study of polecats' use of farmyards and farm buildings (places where the animals are most likely to encounter rodenticides) and wide-scale screening of rodenticide residues in road casualty polecats. These studies are published elsewhere (Shore et al., 1996, in press 1999; Birks, 1998). However, the main findings of these studies are included in summarised form in the results section below.

An important aspect of the ecology of polecats on lowland farmland concerns their interaction with human activities and commercial interests. The ways in which the polecat might be seen to conflict with such interests, whether false or real, might adversely affect tolerance of the current recovery among key sectors of the rural community. Negative attitudes might lead to persecution threatening the conservation of the species as they did in the past (Langley & Yalden, 1977). A questionnaire survey of the attitudes, practices and experiences of farmers and gamekeepers was undertaken as part of the VWT study and is published elsewhere (Packer & Birks, 1999). The main findings of this exercise are also summarised in this section.

8.2 Methods

8.2.1 Radio-tracking

During 1993, 1994 and 1995 wild polecats were live-trapped and radio-tracked in two areas of lowland farmland in the west of England. The first was a landscape dominated by stock farming centred on the Parish of Mathon on the Herefordshire/Worcestershire border; the other was a mixed farming landscape including intensive arable cropping centred on the Parish of Kemerton on the borders of Worcestershire and Gloucestershire. Most fieldwork was carried out in the former area where mean farm-holding size was 57ha. Land use in both areas was dominated by agriculture, though each contained a range of semi-natural habitat features (hedgerows, plantations, wetlands and woodlands). Rabbits were common in both study areas. Polecats are thought to have recolonised the Mathon study area in the late 1960s, and the Kemerton area in the late 1970s.

Polecats were live-trapped under licence from English Nature in single-entry cage traps designed for mink and common rats. Trapped polecats were sedated with 'Domitor'[7], and fitted with TW-3 radio collars[8]. The sedation procedure is regulated under the Animals (Scientific Procedures) Act 1986, so Home Office licences were required for this work. Radio-collared animals were monitored by means of hand-held 3-element Yagi aerials and Mariner Radar M-57 receivers usually deployed by researchers on foot. Radio-tracking was carried out in continuous sessions of variable duration (1-5 hours) during the hours of darkness when polecats are most active (Blandford & Walton, 1991a). In daylight, occasional locations were recorded to confirm inactivity and to identify resting sites. During continuous

Plate 12.
The VWT's polecat radio-tracking study in the west of England:

a) the Parish of Mathon in Herefordshire where most of the radio-tracking was carried out

b) Damien Offer radio-tracking in the Kemerton study area in south Worcestershire, with views across the Severn Vale to the Malvern Hills

c) nearly half of the polecats radio-tracked between October and February concentrated on foraging for rats in farmyards like this

d) in winter, polecats used barns filled with hay or straw as daytime resting sites.

[7] SmithKline Beecham Animal Health Ltd, Tadworth, Surrey KT20 7NT, UK.
[8] All radio-tracking equipment was supplied by BIOTRACK, Wareham, Dorset, UK.

radio-tracking sessions details of the animals' location, habitat occupied and level of activity were recorded at minimum intervals of 15 minutes in line with other studies (Harris *et al.*, 1990). When recording these 'fixes' animals were classified as either active or inactive according to the presence or absence of significant variations in radio signal strength (see Kenward, 1987).

Habitat use in both study areas combined was analysed by means of compositional analysis - a method of determining habitat preference from radio-tracking data (Aebischer & Robertson, 1992; Aebischer *et al.*, 1993). Polecats' use of seven habitat categories, revealed by the distribution of radio fixes, was compared with the availability of habitats within Minimum Convex Polygon (MCP) home ranges. To maximise data independence, radio fixes from each individual used for this analysis comprised a sub-sample of a maximum three night-time and one daytime fixes from each 24 hour period, with all fixes separated by a minimum of 60 minutes. In the case of three animals, this sampling process led to the number of fixes falling slightly below the 30 recommended by Aebischer *et al*. (1993). Some data on habitat use are also presented in the form of proportions of all fixes recorded.

Radio collars were normally recovered for re-use by re-trapping animals after 3-4 weeks of radio-tracking. Occasionally collars were shed by polecats during radio-tracking. One male became adept at removing his collar by reversing between tightly-packed bales in a haystack. The problem of collar-shedding is common in radio-tracking studies of small mustelids, because the study animals tend to have necks and heads of similar diameter.

8.2.2 Dietary analysis

In an exercise co-ordinated by the VWT (see Section 5), polecat corpses were gathered in the English Midlands by volunteers over the period 1993-1997. Details of sex, cause of death, date of recovery and location were recorded for each corpse recovered. Most were road casualties; some of these were badly damaged to the extent that internal organs were not recoverable. Relatively intact corpses were processed at the Royal Museum of Scotland (Edinburgh), where stomachs and intestines were dissected out for analysis. Stomach contents were removed and weighed. Samples weighing less than 1g (wet weight) were classed as 'empty'. Individual stomach content samples were examined visually under a binocular microscope, and prey remains were separated where more than one prey category was present. Where necessary to aid identification, samples were washed over a fine mesh sieve (aperture 53μm) in warm tap water and detergent. Hair and feathers were examined under a microscope and identified using keys published by Day (1966) and Teerink (1991). In addition, a reference collection of slides of common prey species was prepared to aid identification. Having identified prey to species where possible, the percentage volume of each category present in each sample was estimated to the nearest 10%. Samples which could not be identified were recorded and quantified as such. A note was made of miscellaneous items such as plant and mineral material.

Some polecat faeces were collected from daytime resting sites identified during radio-tracking. Contents were identified under a binocular microscope by reference to published keys (see above). Estimates of dietary composition were calculated on the basis of frequency of occurrence and estimated percentage bulk of undigested remains (Wise *et al*., 1981).

8.3 Results

Behavioural data were collected from 13 polecats (nine males and four females) over 17 radio-tracking periods. These are summarised in Table 8.1. Most animals were radio-tracked only once. However, two were tracked on two separate occasions and one, M.G, was tracked three times in different seasons. Polecats were considerably easier to trap in autumn, winter and spring than in summer. As a result the summer months are poorly represented in the radio-tracking data.

8.3.1 Habitat use

Compositional analysis of radio-tracking data illustrates the degree of selection by polecats for the habitats available to them within MCP home ranges. Use of habitats was non-random (Wilk's lambda $=0.445$; $p=0.006$). The data presented in Table 8.2 show that the most preferred habitat was 'woodland edge' (defined here as the peripheral five metres of any woodland, plantation or area of scrub). This habitat, together with agricultural premises (farmyards, barns etc.), field boundaries and wetlands, was selected significantly more than non-edge woodland, suburban areas and open fields (the last being the least preferred habitat). Polecats appeared actively to avoid travelling across large areas of open ground. Subjectively, the preference for woodland edge and field boundary habitats can be explained largely by the concentrations of rabbits and rabbit warrens they supported in both study areas.

114

Table 8.1. A summary of 17 radio-tracking sessions involving 13 polecats in the west of England (* animals radio-tracked on more than one occasion are numbered to indicate different tracking sessions in chronological order). M prefixes indicate males; F prefixes indicate females.

Study area and animal	Approx. age (years)	MCP home range size (ha.)	Number of days tracked	Number of fixes	Tracking period	Number of different daytime resting sites used	% fixes in rabbit warrens	% fixes in agricultural premises	Number of 1km squares of OS grid occupied
Mathon									
M. Bru	1+	500	47	70	Sep-Nov	21	58.75	3.7	11
F. Mi	<1	56	24	36	Oct-Nov	7	2.7	86.5	4
F. Me	1+	375	44	58	Oct-Dec	12	29.0	46.8	9
M. Bra	<1	178	25	48	Nov-Dec	9	54.2	18.7	4
M. G (1)*	1+	481	34	72	Mar-Apr	16	32.9	9.6	11
M. G (2)*	2+	350	41	179	Jun-Jul	19	25.7	0.0	7
M. Je	<1	225	27	106	Sep-Oct	22	66.0	0.0	7
M. Ji	<1	250	38	139	Sep-Oct	21	53.9	9.1	6
M. D (1)*	<1	16	22	112	Nov-Dec	8	0.9	99.1	2
M. G (3)*	2+	153	26	108	Nov-Dec	8	35.2	61.1	5
M. D (2)*	<1	131	36	162	Jan-Feb	11	90.7	0.6	6
Kemerton									
F. L (1)*	1+	25	41	27	Nov-Jan	10	92.6	0.0	2
F. T	<1	41	38	25	Dec-Jan	11	92.0	0.0	3
M. H	<1	216	30	21	Jan-Feb	9	71.4	4.8	6
F. L (2)*	2+	28	36	56	Sep-Nov	10	48.2	1.8	2
M. B	<1	53	43	94	Sep-Nov	11	86.2	1.1	3
M. Ge	<1	28	19	57	Nov-Dec	4	19.3	64.9	2

Table 8.2. Ranking matrix of means and standard errors of log-ratio differences between habitat categories utilised by 13 polecats (from radio fixes) and habitat categories available within MCP home ranges.
Significant differences (p<0.05) are shown in bold. The overall rank of each habitat is shown in the final column, (rank 6 indicates the most preferred habitat).

	Agricultural premises	Field boundaries	Wetlands	Woodland	Woodland edge	Suburban	Open fields	Rank
Agricultural premises		0.14±0.37	0.51±0.51	**0.97±0.36**	-0.21±0.49	**2.73±0.46**	**3.97±0.5**	5
Field boundaries	-0.14±0.37		0.36±0.45	0.82±0.40	-0.35±0.46	**2.59±0.51**	**3.82±0.39**	4
Wetlands	-0.51±0.51	-0.36±0.45		0.46±0.4	-0.71±0.39	**2.22±0.39**	**3.46±0.33**	3
Woodland	**-0.97±0.36**	-0.82±0.40	-0.46±0.4		**-1.18±0.51**	**1.76±0.45**	**3.0±0.39**	2
Woodland edge	0.21±0.49	0.35±0.46	0.71±0.39	**1.18±0.51**		**2.94±0.37**	**4.18±0.36**	6
Suburban	**-2.73±0.46**	**-2.59±0.51**	**-2.22±0.39**	**-1.76±0.45**	**-2.94±0.37**		**1.24±0.38**	1
Open fields	**-4.68±0.39**	**-4.12±0.43**	**-3.56±0.396**	**-3.50±0.365**	**-4.53±0.384**	**-1.70±0.254**		0

Some seasonal variations in habitat use by polecats were apparent from the radio-tracking data. Compositional analysis of a 'winter' (October - February) sub-set of the data in Table 8.2, published in a study of rodenticide contamination risk (Birks, 1998), showed that the ranking of the two most preferred habitats was reversed. Thus, in winter, agricultural premises emerged as the most preferred habitat among polecats on lowland farmland. A simpler breakdown of habitat use (see Figure 8.1) illustrates the extent to which use of agricultural premises is concentrated in the 'winter' half of the year.

8.3.2 Population density

Extensive trapping in the Mathon study area with the main aim of catching polecats for radio-tracking allowed a crude estimate of numbers per unit area. A mean population density of approximately 0.5-1.0 polecats per km^2 existed during the period of study. The issue of population density is considered at greater length in Section 6.

8.3.3 Home range size

Although tracking periods were relatively short, all radio-tracked polecats were apparently resident in home ranges rather than dispersing. MCP home range sizes for all radio-tracking sessions are presented in Table 8.1. Male ranges tended to be larger (mean 212.3±143.4ha, n=9) than those of females (mean 124.625±167.35ha, n=4), though samples were too small to allow statistical comparison. It is also apparent from Table 8.1 that first-winter polecats tended to occupy smaller home ranges than older animals.

In view of the need to develop a method of monitoring polecat abundance, described in Section 6, radio-tracking data were used to examine the ways in which polecats moved in relation to the sampling unit based on the 1km squares of the OS grid (see Table 8.3). Animals occupying stable home ranges commonly ranged over several (up to a maximum of 11) 1km squares. No difference was found in the number of squares visited by male and female polecats (t=0.26, df=15, p>0.05).

116

Figure 8.1. The distribution of fixes from 13 radio-tracked polecats across broad habitat categories on lowland farmland, showing seasonal variation in the use of agricultural premises.

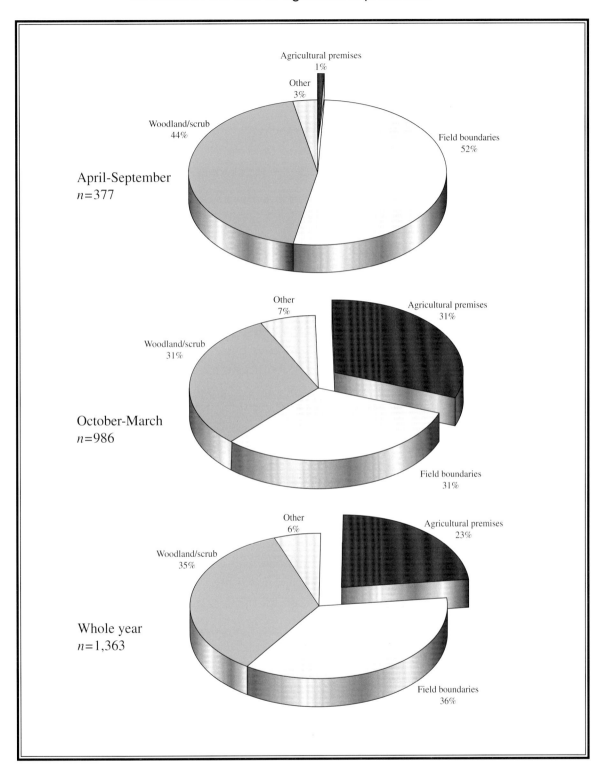

Nearly half (47.8%) of all 1km squares visited by polecats were visited only occasionally and briefly in each radio-tracking session (in this study the term 'radio-tracking session' is used to describe the entire period in a given season in which one individual is monitored before removal of its radio collar). Exclusion of these 'peripheral' squares (defined as all 1km squares containing fewer than three radio locations during a radio-tracking session) leaves a smaller sample of 'main' squares in which the majority of radio-tracked polecats' time was spent (see Table 8.3). As with the total sample of squares visited, there was no apparent difference in the number of 'main' squares visited by male and female polecats ($t = 0.19$, $df=15$, $p>0.05$).

Table 8.3. Mean numbers of 1km squares of the OS grid visited by polecats during 17 radio-tracking sessions ('main' squares exclude those with three radio locations or less).

	Mean number of 1km squares visited during each session	Mean number of 'main' 1km squares visited
Males (*n*=12)	5.8±3.0	3.2±2.1
Females (*n*=5)	4.0±2.9	1.8±0.8
All sessions	5.3±3.0	2.8±1.9

8.3.4 Timing of activity

This study was not designed to collect data on activity patterns. However, information gathered incidentally points to a marked nocturnality that has been reported by other authors. Considering all radio fixes, polecats were active for 31.8% of recorded time (this must be regarded as an exaggeration because radio-tracking was concentrated mainly in the hours of darkness when the animals were more likely to be active). 72.4% of all recorded activity occurred during the hours of darkness. Where polecat activity was recorded in daylight, the great majority would have been essentially invisible to human observers. For example, in agricultural premises all daytime activity (11.4% of recorded activity in this habitat) involved polecats within or beneath barns or haystacks. In rural habitats, 45.9% of daytime activity involved animals underground in rabbit warrens and 40.5% involved animals within areas of woodland and scrub. Typically, polecats were largely inactive within secure resting sites during daylight. Most foraging and travelling within the home range occurred after nightfall.

8.3.5 Resting sites

The data in Table 8.1 show that radio-tagged polecats each used many different resting sites within stable home ranges (eg. one sub-adult male, M.Je, used 22 different daytime resting sites over a 27-day period). 186 resting sites were identified and assigned to the categories illustrated in Figure 8.2. A further 23 resting sites could only be located approximately and could not be accurately identified. Rabbit warrens or burrows were the

Figure 8.2. The frequency of occurrence of daytime resting sites used by radio-tagged polecats on lowland farmland (*n*=209).

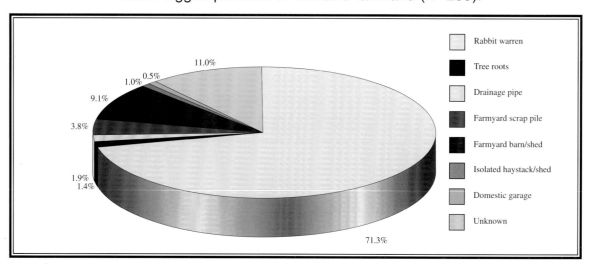

commonest resting sites, accounting for 80% of identified sites. Every radio-tagged polecat made some use of rabbit warrens as resting sites. Warrens were typically 'active' (that is, showing signs of use by rabbits) and polecats often lived in them and preyed on the inhabitants (see Section 8.3.8). The remaining identifiable resting sites were largely in human-made structures such as barns, haystacks and drains.

No resting sites were encountered that had been excavated by polecats. All were existing cavities or burrows used opportunistically and without obvious modification. Bedding collection was observed in one case, where a male polecat occupied a dry field drain for one day and gathered dried grass and leaves from within 0.5m of the entrance to construct a temporary nest inside. Only very rarely did field signs (eg. droppings) at the entrance of occupied resting sites suggest the presence of a radio-tagged polecat. Thus, resting sites used by polecats in this study typically showed no external evidence of the animals' presence.

8.3.6 Use of farmyards and buildings (based on a summary of data from Birks, 1998)

Most radio-tagged polecats (11 of the 13 individuals tracked) made some use of agricultural premises, defined here as farmyards and isolated farm buildings or structures such as haystacks. Use of such premises was apparently concentrated in the winter months with a peak in November (see Figure 8.3). 45.4% of radio-tagged polecats between October and February were heavy users of agricultural premises, spending over 40% of recorded time in this habitat (see Table 8.1). Despite this winter pattern, there was no evidence of an association between use of farm buildings and periods when the air temperature fell to 0.0° Celsius or below ($t=0.548$, $df=329$, $p>0.05$).

Figure 8.3. Monthly variation in the use of agricultural premises by radio-tagged polecats.

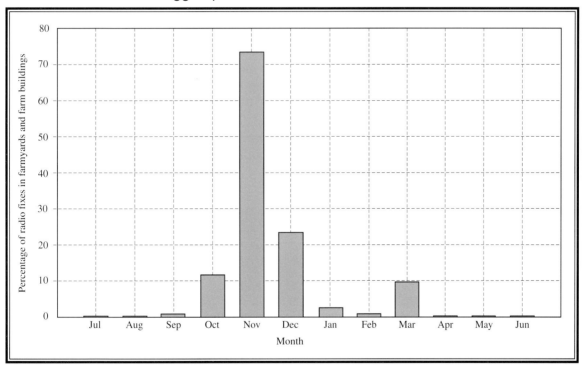

Polecats used agricultural premises for both foraging and resting, and some individuals spent several consecutive days and nights in such places. The most frequently used daytime resting sites in agricultural premises were barns containing stacks of hay (accounting for 60.6% of 'polecat days' in agricultural premises). Less-common resting sites included straw and grain stores, cow and machinery sheds and piles of farmyard rubble and scrap. Activity by polecats in agricultural premises tended to focus upon areas where rodent activity was concentrated, such as sheds and barns used for housing stock, grain and hay (see Figure 8.4).

Figure 8.4. The distribution of polecat activity across six location categories within farmyards.

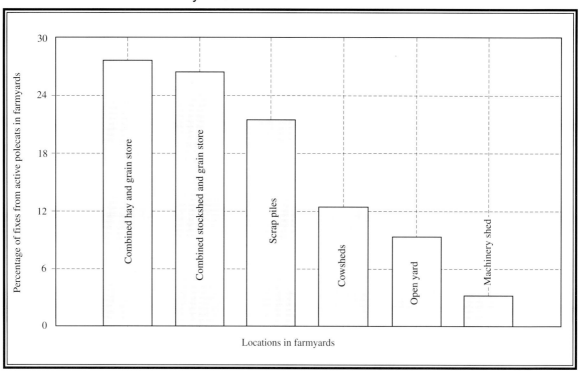

It was easy to collect scats from haystacks where polecats rested because latrine areas were progressively revealed as hay was removed over the winter to be fed to livestock. Analysis of 237 polecat scats from such sites was used to determine the diet of these farmyard-using animals. This is illustrated in Figure 8.5, expressed as the percentage bulk of undigested identifiable prey remains, revealing that common rats dominated the diet. These data cannot be regarded as representative of polecat diet generally, because they are clearly biased towards those animals which spent a great deal of time in farmyards, rather than in open countryside where a different range of prey might be encountered.

Figure 8.5. The diet of farmyard-using polecats based on analysis of 237 scats collected from farmyard dens used by radio-tagged polecats.

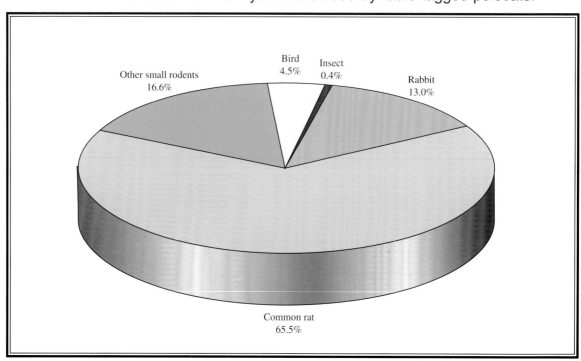

This dietary evidence supports the view that foraging by polecats for winter concentrations of rats and other rodents explains their pattern of use of agricultural premises. It also confirms the likely route of contamination of polecats with anticoagulant rodenticides. Half of the farmers questioned in the Mathon and Kemerton study areas reported using rodenticides in winter to control rats and mice around farm buildings. All used the more toxic 'second generation' rodenticides, such as difenacoum, which have largely replaced warfarin. Radio-tagged polecats visited all farmyards in which rodenticides were applied regularly in the two study areas, as well as some farmyards where these chemicals were used infrequently or not at all. 45.4% of polecats radio-tracked in winter were regarded as vulnerable to rodenticide contamination, because they made heavy use (>40% of recorded time) of farmyards where rodenticides were applied regularly.

13 out of 20 farmyards supported low rat populations during the study, but one ('farmyard X') supported a particularly heavy infestation. This farmyard was used more than any other by radio-tagged polecats (by four animals over two winters). One sub-adult female (F.Mi) died during radio-tracking in farmyard X and a subsequent post-mortem revealed a liver concentration of 1.4mg/kg of difenacoum, the active ingredient in the brand of rodenticide used in the farmyard. An adult male (M.G) was killed by a car after spending time foraging in farmyard X. Subsequent analysis revealed a liver concentration in this animal of 0.3mg/kg of difenacoum.

Farmyard X was also distinguished by being the only one in which two radio-tagged polecats were recorded simultaneously. During November and December 1994 two apparently unrelated radio-tagged males, sub-adult M.D and adult M.G, occupied home ranges which included farmyard X. Over the 13 days when radio-tracking sessions of these animals overlapped, both were located in farmyard X together on 11 days. 19 simultaneous locations for both animals were recorded, each relating to separate bouts of resting or foraging activity over the 11 days. On six of these occasions the two males were located within the farmyard but more than 50m apart, resting or foraging in or near separate areas of rat activity. However, on the remaining 13 occasions they were located within 15m of each other, and on three of these they were located in the same rat-infested barn used for storing grain and hay. Two consecutive daytime radio-tracking sessions revealed that both animals were resting in this barn approximately two metres apart in the same small stack of hay bales.

One other instance of two polecats apparently using the same farmyard was recorded in the Kemerton study area, when a non-radio-tagged female was live-trapped in December 1994 in the same barn as was being used as a resting place by a radio-tagged male M.Ge.

This study was not designed to study social interactions between polecats and no attempts were made to radio-track several animals concurrently. Thus, there may have been further unrevealed instances of two or more polecats exploiting agricultural premises concurrently.

8.3.7 Rodenticide residues in polecats (based on a summary of data from Shore *et al.*, 1996, in press 1999)

In the light of evidence (see Section 8.3.6) of potentially lethal exposure to modern rodenticides a sample of dead polecats (mostly recovered as mid-1990s road casualties from the English Midlands) was screened in collaboration with the ITE. Thirteen livers (26%) of 50 polecats recovered from seven English counties contained detectable residues of three rodenticides. Difenacoum and bromadiolone were the predominant compounds and were detected in 16% and 14% of animals respectively. Brodifacoum was found in only one animal and flocoumafen was not detected in any animals. Both sexes appeared equally likely to be exposed to rodenticides. Contaminated polecats were recovered from Herefordshire, Worcestershire, Gloucestershire, Oxfordshire and Buckinghamshire. The proportion of contaminated animals recovered was highest between November and April, the period when animals are thought most likely to encounter rodenticides whilst foraging in farmyards.

8.3.8 Levels of use of rabbit warrens by polecats

Radio-tracking revealed a strong association between polecats and rabbit warrens on farmland. Approximately half of all radio fixes in this study were recorded from polecats in rabbit burrows or warrens (see Table 8.4). It is likely that this is an underestimate of the extent of warren use, because on many occasions the need to avoid disturbing an active polecat by approaching too closely, or difficulties posed by darkness, prevented its precise location within or outside burrows by radio-tracking at close range. Thus, 40.4% of precise night-time locations (as opposed to broad habitat categories) of polecats in rural habitats were classed as 'unknown'.

Table 8.4. The proportion of radio fixes recorded from polecats occupying rabbit warrens (data from both study areas combined).

Polecat activity category	Proportion of all non-farmyard fixes* recorded from rabbit warrens		Proportion of all fixes recorded from rabbit warrens	
Active	35.8%	($n = 363$)	29.9%	($n = 434$)
Inactive	79.0%	($n = 690$)	58.7%	($n = 929$)
Total	64.1%	($n = 1,053$)	49.5%	($n = 1,363$)

* This sample excludes all fixes from polecats within agricultural premises.

8.3.8.1 Patterns of polecat activity within warrens

There was ample evidence that polecat activity within rabbit warrens involved foraging. For example, on several occasions when a polecat was recorded as active underground, rabbits were heard 'thumping' in alarm. On two occasions during daylight, rabbits were observed bolting from warrens in response to an active radio-tagged polecat underground. 60.8% of recorded polecat activity in rabbit warrens occurred during the hours of darkness, though this figure may be an underestimate due to the practical difficulties outlined above.

Excluding those from agricultural premises, nearly 80% of inactive fixes were recorded from polecats underground in rabbit warrens. These were the most frequently used daytime resting sites (see Table 8.5), accounting for 54.8% of locations of polecats in daylight hours (73.6% if daytime fixes from agricultural premises are excluded).

Table 8.5. Use of rabbit warrens by polecats as daytime resting sites, expressed as a percentage of all radio fixes recorded during daylight across two seasons in each study area.

Study area	'Summer' (April - September)		'Winter' (October - March)		Whole year	
Kemerton	40.0%	($n = 5$)	75.2%	($n = 149$)	74.0%	($n = 154$)
Mathon	52.9%	($n = 138$)	44.1%	($n = 254$)	47.2%	($n = 392$)
Both combined	52.4%	($n = 143$)	55.6%	($n = 403$)	54.8%	($n = 546$)

8.3.8.2 Variations in patterns of rabbit warren use

All radio-tagged polecats in this study made use of rabbit warrens. There was no seasonal difference in the extent of this behaviour. Rabbit warrens accounted for 50.4% of 'winter' fixes and 47.1% of 'summer' fixes (Yates' corrected Chi square=0.3, *df*=1, *p*>0.5). Nor did use of rabbit warrens differ between the sexes. 50.1% of male polecat fixes were recorded from rabbit warrens, compared with 46.1% of female fixes (Yates' corrected Chi square=0.8, *df*=1, *p*>0.2). The balance of polecat activity and inactivity within rabbit warrens was also similar in both sexes (Chi square=0.29, *df*=3, *p*>0.5)

However, there were some individual variations in the extent of warren use. The proportion of fixes recorded from individuals in rabbit warrens varied considerably, though the majority of polecats spent well over 50% of recorded time in rabbit warrens (see Table 8.1). Most radio-tagged polecats made use of a number of different rabbit warrens within their home ranges, normally being recorded in the same warren over one to three consecutive 24 hour periods before moving on (see Figure 8.6). One sub-adult female in the Kemerton study area, however, was recorded in the same warren and nowhere else over an 18-day period.

Figure 8.6. The number of consecutive 24-hour periods over which rabbit warrens were occupied as daytime resting sites by individual radio-tagged polecats.

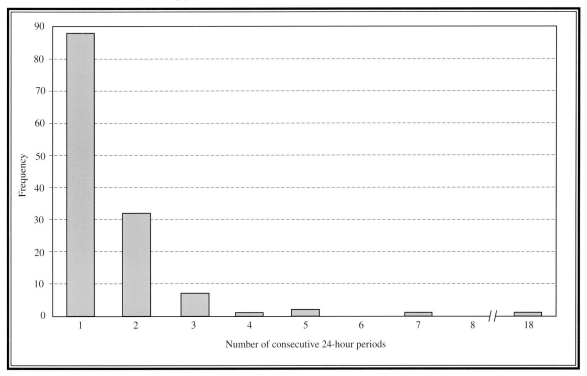

8.3.9 Awareness of polecats among the rural community

At the start of this study in 1993 a census was carried out of the owners and/or managers of 24 farm units in the Mathon study area. All were asked whether they were aware of polecats on their land and whether they had ever seen them in their agricultural premises. Only two were aware of the presence of polecats on their land (one of these because his gamekeeper had recently trapped some) and only one of these (the manager of a pig farm) had ever seen a live polecat in his farmyard, which was subsequently found dead. This lack of contact with the species is perhaps unsurprising given the nocturnality of farmyard polecats described above.

During the course of the study live-trapped polecats were shown to most landowners, and radio-tracking operations raised awareness among the agricultural community of the animal's use of farmyards. Despite the interest thus generated, no farmers or farm workers reported seeing live polecats in agricultural premises during the two-year duration of the study. Although a full census of the Kemerton study area was not undertaken, it appeared that both the visibility of polecats, and farmers' awareness of them, were similarly low. During the radio-tracking study, when JDSB was partly nocturnal and frequently drove around both study areas at night, free-ranging polecats (including radio-tagged animals) were seen on no more than five occasions.

8.3.10 Occurrence of feral or escaped ferrets

Over three years in the more intensively-studied Mathon area five ferrets were recovered. All were apparently underweight and in poor physical condition. One female was found dead with severe bite wounds to the nape of the neck consistent with recent mating injuries. The remainder were recovered alive. All were relatively tame and desperate for food (one entered a shed and killed six ducks before it was live-trapped). These were clearly recently escaped animals rather than members of a feral population.

8.3.11 Diet of polecats in England

Despite intensive radio-tracking of polecats in two study areas, very few polecat scats were found outside the haystack resting sites described above. Searches of the entrances of other daytime resting sites, and of areas used by foraging polecats a few hours previously, very rarely revealed scats. Destruction of resting sites in order to recover scats was felt to be too disturbing to the study animals. As a result, information on the diet of radio-tagged polecats was limited to those making heavy use of farmyards where adequate numbers of scats could be recovered (see Section 8.3.6). Data from these animals were likely to be dominated by farmyard prey and would not, therefore, reflect the dietary composition of the wider population. A source of more general information on polecat diet was available, however, in the form of stomach contents recovered from dead animals collected during the recording exercise described in Section 5.

A total of 133 polecat stomachs from England, mostly from road casualty animals, was examined. Fifty of these were either empty or contained only traces of unidentifiable

Figure 8.7. The source of polecat stomachs used for diet analysis, showing the proportion containing rabbit remains.

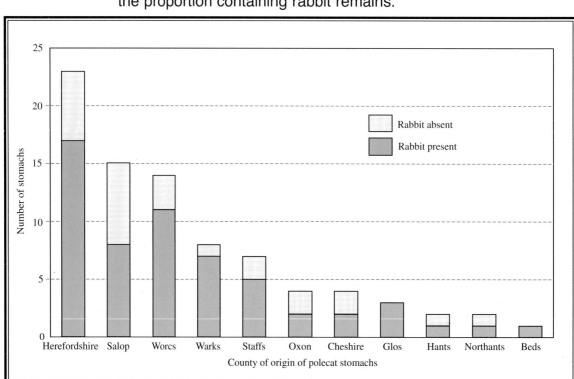

Table 8.6. A summary of the stomach contents of road casualty polecats from the English Midlands in the 1990s.

Prey type	Total diet (n=83 stomachs)				Males only (n=53 stomachs)				Females only (n=30 stomachs)			
	weight (g)	% weight	f	% stomachs	weight (g)	% weight	f	% stomachs	weight (g)	% weight	f	% stomachs
Rabbit	1063.8	85.4	60	72.3	897.62	88.6	42	79.2	166.18	71.3	18	60.0
Polecat	4.5	0.4	1	1.2	0.0	0.0	0	0.0	4.5	1.9	1	3.3
Common rat	22.18	1.8	2	2.4	13.91	1.4	1	1.9	8.27	3.5	1	3.3
Bat	2.54	0.2	1	1.2	2.54	0.2	1	1.9	0.0	0.0	0	0.0
Field vole	21.21	1.7	2	2.4	10.21	1.0	1	1.9	11.0	4.7	1	3.3
Bank vole	3.33	0.3	1	1.2	0.0	0.0	0	0.0	3.33	1.4	1	3.3
Wood mouse	11.85	1.0	3	3.6	10.21	1.0	1	1.9	1.64	0.7	1	3.3
Unident. small mammal	0.11	0.01	1	1.2	0.0	0.0	0	0.0	0.11	0.05	1	3.3
Total Mammals	**1129.52**	**90.7**	**71**		**934.49**	**92.2**	**46**		**195.03**	**83.6**	**24**	
Columbiformes	29.45	2.4	3	3.6	1.97	0.2	1	1.9	27.48	11.8	2	6.7
Passeriformes	0.42	0.03	2	2.4	0.34	0.03	1	1.9	0.08	0.03	1	3.3
Charadriiformes	0.21	0.03	1	1.2	0.21	0.02	1	1.9	0.0	0.0	0	0.0
Unident. bird	7.16	0.06	2	2.4	4.48	0.4	1	1.9	2.68	1.1	1	3.3
Total Birds	**37.24**	**3**	**8**		**7.0**	**0.7**	**4**		**30.24**	**13.0**	**4**	
Amphibians	56.98	4.6	7	8.4	50.68	5	5	9.4	6.3	2.7	2	6.7
Fish	0.12	0.01	1	1.2	0.0	0.0	0	0.0	0.12	0.05	1	3.3
Earthworms	21.97	1.8	2	2.4	20.46	2	1	1.9	1.51	0.6	1	3.3
Total	**1245.83**		**89**		**1012.63**		**56**		**233.20**		**32**	

remains; these were excluded from subsequent analyses. The 83 stomachs containing identifiable remains were recovered from 11 English counties, though the majority (63%) were derived from the three western counties of Herefordshire, Shropshire and Worcestershire (see Figure 8.7).

Data on polecat stomach contents are presented in Table 8.6 and summarised in Figure 8.8. Rabbits clearly dominated the diet of polecats in this sample, occurring in 72.3% of stomachs and comprising 85.4% of the weight of prey remains identified. Most stomachs analysed (67.5% of the total and 93.3% of those containing rabbit) contained nothing but rabbit remains. The occurrence of rabbit remains in polecat stomachs was geographically widespread (see Figure 8.7). Other prey inevitably made relatively minor contributions, with amphibians (only frogs and toads were identified) being the second most significant prey category. The single occurrence of polecat remains probably involved an animal ingested as carrion. These remains were identified together with blowfly larvae in the stomach of a female polecat road casualty recovered from Worcestershire in the summer months.

Figure 8.8. The diet of polecats in England, expressed as % bulk of remains identified in stomachs of road casualty animals (*n*=83).

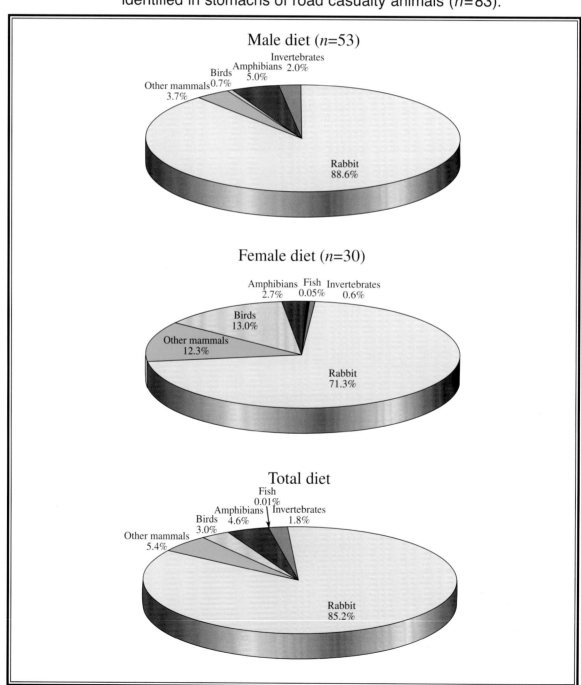

Figure 8.8 illustrates the occurrence of the main prey categories for male and female polecats separately. Although females tended to take more non-rabbit mammals and birds than did males, there was no significant difference between the sexes in the frequency of occurrence of rabbits, other mammals, birds and amphibians (Chi square=4.43, df=7, p>0.05). Although rabbits were recorded in polecat stomachs in each season of the year (see Figure 8.9), there was some seasonal variation in the frequency of occurrence. The greatest proportion of stomachs contained rabbit in spring and the least in autumn (Chi square=15.32, df=7, p<0.05). Surprisingly, all occurrences of amphibians in stomachs occurred in the autumn sample, rather than in the spring (see Figure 8.9).

Figure 8.9. Seasonal variation in the occurrence of rabbit and amphibian remains in the stomachs of English polecats.

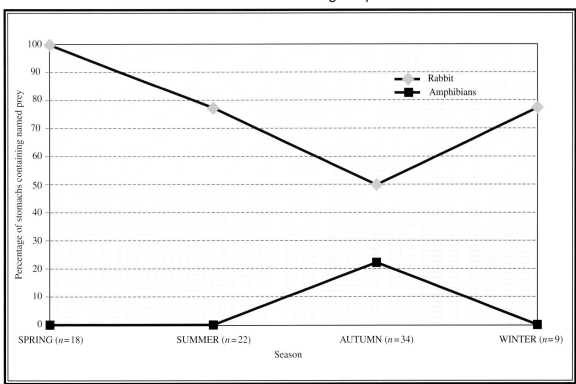

8.3.12 A summary of farmers' and gamekeepers' attitudes towards polecats (based on data from Packer & Birks, 1999)

In 1996 the VWT initiated postal questionnaire surveys among farmers and gamekeepers through ADAS and BASC. Responses were received from 335 farmers (27% of questionnaires sent) and 66 gamekeepers (30%) from within the polecat's main range in Wales and the English West Midlands. Only 11% of farmers had ever experienced damage to stock by polecats. In contrast, 66.6% of gamekeepers had experienced predation of penned game by polecats. Of these, 68% believed polecats entered game pens via the 'pop-holes' designed to allow pheasants to run back into the pen at ground level.

Most gamekeepers (67.7%) described the polecat as a minor pest and ranked it as a less serious enemy of game than other predators except the common rat and hedgehog. Gamekeepers near the fringes of the polecat's range were more likely to feel indifferent or neutral about the species than those in the core of its range. 65% of farmers believed polecats killed or injured game on the farm. However, 61% felt they helped to control rabbits and 53% felt they helped to control rodents on the farm. 39% agreed that the polecat was an interesting species to have on the farm.

80% of gamekeepers (91% of those with experience of polecats) had trapped polecats over the preceding five years. 95.4% of gamekeepers wished to be free to control polecats whenever problems occurred. The commonest response among gamekeepers to a hypothetical problem of polecat predation of penned game would be to increase the number of lethal tunnel traps set around game pens. This was followed by night-time closure of pop-holes. 67.5% of farmers felt they should be free to control polecats. Farmers used traps, shooting and dogs to control polecats. These control efforts were more prevalent on farms near the fringe of the polecat's range compared with the core.

8.4 Discussion

Many European studies have drawn attention to the polecat's association with small rodents or with semi-aquatic habitats and prey (see reviews by Blandford, 1987; Weber, 1989; Lodé, 1997). Evidence gathered during the VWT study suggests that polecat ecology in Britain does not conform to this pattern, perhaps due to the widescale loss of lowland wetlands since the 1950s (Anon. 1984). Compositional analysis indicated that 'wetlands' ranked fourth in preference terms out of seven habitat categories available to radio-tagged polecats. Also, small rodents and semi-aquatic prey each comprised less than 7% of the diet of polecats collected from England during the 1990s. Rather, this study has revealed that the rabbit is a key element in the ecology of the polecat in lowland Britain. In his analysis of polecat diet data from 18 sites throughout Europe, Lodé (1997) found only one area, the Camargue in southern France, with a comparable preponderance of rabbits.

Rabbits provided the great majority of two essential resources for polecats in this study - food and resting sites. Blandford's (1986) mid-Wales study revealed a similar association, with lagomorphs comprising 63% (and amphibians only 3.9%) of the corrected estimated bulk of prey in scats of radio-tagged polecats, and rabbit burrows comprising 49% of 106 polecat dens identified during radio-tracking. Conversely, Walton's (1968a) analysis of polecat stomach contents in the mid-1960s, when rabbit numbers in Wales were still depressed following myxomatosis (Trout *et al.*, 1986), revealed a more diverse diet. Mammals comprised 35.1% of prey occurrences (lagomorph percentage was not specified) compared with amphibians at 26.3%. It seems likely that the relatively great abundance of rabbits in Britain explains much of the observed difference in polecat ecology between British and European populations.

The polecat's successful exploitation of both rabbits and their warrens on farmland is clearly an important factor in the species' current recovery in Britain. In addition, the consumption in winter of farmyard rats is a significant component of polecat ecology. However, there are some risks associated with such a close relationship with these two major agricultural pests.

8.4.1 Implications of wild rabbit management for polecat conservation

Following its recovery from myxomatosis, the rabbit has been increasing in numbers in Britain and is once more a major agricultural pest (Trout *et al.*, 1986; Trout, 1994). 80% of farmers employ rabbit control and management techniques in order to limit economic damage to crops (Trout, 1994). Increasingly, non-agricultural land managers are also adopting control measures as a legal requirement, for example, to limit rabbit damage to railway and road embankments (Edwards, 1997). It is inevitable that some of these measures will accidentally affect the polecat. For example, 12 polecat records from the 1990s related to animals found in cage traps set for rabbits (see Section 5.3.2.3).

The polecat's frequent use of active rabbit warrens for foraging and as daytime resting sites on farmland makes the species vulnerable to those methods of rabbit control which focus on burrow systems. Neither trapping in rabbit burrow entrances with lethal spring traps, nor 'warren ripping' (the destruction of burrow systems with heavy machinery) nor 'warren drowning' (flooding warrens with farmyard effluents) are currently in common use in Britain, though records considered in Section 5.3.2 include one of a polecat killed in a spring trap set in a rabbit burrow (this style of trapping is apparently common in parts of East

Anglia - J. Reynolds, pers. comm.). Fumigation of rabbit burrows with toxic gas, however, is regarded as one of the most effective control methods and is commonly recommended by advisers and statutory agencies (R. Trout, pers. comm.). Approximately 27% of farmers in England and Wales use burrow fumigation to control rabbits (Trout, 1994).

Non-target mortality arising from burrow fumigation is impossible to monitor because any corpses would normally remain entombed within rabbit burrow systems. One case of suspected accidental exposure to burrow fumigant was recorded during the VWT study. A dying polecat exhibiting blindness and respiratory distress was found wandering above ground close to a set of rabbit burrows which had been fumigated during the previous 24 hours. Such mortality is likely to become more significant as the polecat extends its range in Britain, since rabbit gassing is practiced more commonly on lowland farms towards the fringes of the species' range than in its Welsh stronghold (Packer & Birks 1999). Furthermore, in the light of evidence that global warming may enhance the future growth of rabbit populations in Britain through the influence of climate on reproduction (Bell & Webb, 1991), one might expect an increase in such rabbit control efforts in future. Non-target mortality among polecats and other predators using rabbit burrows is regrettable, particularly in the light of evidence that predation plays a significant part in regulating wild rabbit numbers on farms in Britain (Trout & Tittensor, 1989).

The polecat's close association with rabbits in Britain raises questions about the likely effects of the sudden removal of such an important resource. The huge reduction in rabbit populations as a consequence of myxomatosis in the 1950s had a considerable effect upon some predators (Sumption & Flowerdew, 1985). Since 1988 a new disease, rabbit haemorrhagic disease (RHD), has reportedly affected many rabbit populations in Europe (Villafuerte et al., 1994) with 'knock-on' effects already apparent upon the breeding success of golden eagles (Fernández, 1993) and red foxes (Villafuerte et al., 1996). RHD was first recorded in Britain in 1992 (Fuller et al., 1993). Early evidence suggests that its impact upon rabbit populations here is less severe than on the European continent (Trout et al., 1997). However, one cannot rule out the possibility of a major epizootic of this or some other rabbit disease in the future. A significant reduction in the availability of rabbits would be expected to have a considerable impact upon polecats. For example, a major human-induced reduction in rabbit numbers in New Zealand led to a significant increase in feral ferret home range size and the proportion of mobile, non-resident animals increased (Norbury et al., 1998). On intensive farmland where alternative prey are scarce a major reduction in rabbit numbers might limit the polecat's ability to establish viable populations. It is also likely to lead to significant intraguild competition, notably with the ecologically similar feral mink.

8.4.2 The rodenticide issue

The polecat's use of agricultural premises for hunting commensal rodents carries a significant and potentially fatal toxicological risk of secondary exposure to anticoagulant rodenticides (Birks, 1998). Studies of the prevalence of rodenticide burdens in British polecats suggests that exposure is widespread. However, current monitoring is inadequate and almost nothing is known about the toxicology and population effects of modern rodenticides in polecats (Shore et al., 1996, in press 1999; Newton et al., 1999). The 26% incidence of rodenticide residues in recovered polecats is considerably lower than that predicted from radio-tracking data, which suggest that 45% of animals are vulnerable. However, sampling based upon road-kills is believed to bias against detection of pesticide residues (Newton et al., 1990). Some affected polecats might not be detected by road casualty-based sampling because the animals either had already died as a consequence of severe contamination (Birks, 1998) or had metabolised and eliminated rodenticide residues to undetectable levels (Shore et al., in press 1999). Shore et al. (in press 1999) indicate that if animals collected between May and October are excluded because it is assumed that residues from the previous winter will have been metabolised, the percentage of contaminated individuals (46%) closely matches that predicted by the radio-tracking data.

Use of rodenticides varies geographically in Britain with a much greater volume applied on farms in the arable-dominated east of England than in the pastoral west (Olney & Garthwaite, 1994). This pattern could hinder the current recovery of the polecat as it extends its range eastwards into areas of greater contamination risk. Indeed, Birks (1998) suggested that where the abundance and variety of prey are limited by intensive farming, polecats could be forced to feed more heavily upon rats carrying harmful doses of rodenticide.

Recent research has confirmed that stoats and weasels are also contaminated by modern rodenticides in Britain (McDonald *et al.*, 1998). Importantly, this work suggested that the route of contamination was via consumption of non-target species such as small 'non-pest' rodents, and revealed that rodenticides were commonly applied away from farm buildings. Thus, polecats may also encounter contaminated prey away from the farmyard situation considered above.

Given the evidence of an unexplained patchy distribution among polecat populations towards the fringe of the species' range (see Section 6), improved understanding of the effects of rodenticide contamination should be viewed as a conservation priority. Proactive monitoring of rodenticide contamination in such vulnerable species is essential and the lack of basic data on exposure, lethal levels and sub-lethal effects of rodenticides in non-target carnivores is deplorable. There is a strong case for requiring ecotoxicological risk assessments of rodenticide usage which extend to considering the full range of non-target effects.

8.5 Acknowledgements

We thank all landowners and farmers who allowed us to work on their farms, including The Kemerton Trust, Overbury Estate, The Elms School, The Downs School, Dr. Phipps, Messrs. Andrews, Armitage, Atkinson, Ballard, Bevan, Blandford, Bowen, Burns, Darby, Doble, Freeman, Green, Hutton, Lewis, Meadows, Nugent, Parker, Perkins, Price, Recordon and Vos.

Special thanks are due to the Lawrences of 'Farmyard X'. We are grateful to Ted Stewart, Craig Stenson and Damien Offer for assistance with fieldwork. We thank Liz Halliwell for help with data analysis. Peter Creber of the Avenue Road Veterinary Practice, Malvern gave valuable veterinary support. We thank Chris Strachan for scat analysis and Catriona McLeod, John Mackenzie and Jacqui Kaye for analysis of polecat stomach contents.

9. RECOMMENDATIONS FOR POLECAT CONSERVATION IN BRITAIN

J.D.S. Birks

9.1 Introduction

The polecat is still a little-known species in Britain and ignorance of the factors likely to promote or hinder its conservation is predictably widespread. Although an encouraging recovery has taken place in recent decades, the polecat's range here remains seriously constricted compared with 150 years ago. Promoting a continuation of that recovery is a sound conservation objective, which fits with the UK Government's obligation under the EC Habitats and Species Directive to achieve a favourable conservation status for the species. The unfavourable or uncertain conservation status of the polecat elsewhere in Europe provides an added incentive to enhance its status in Britain.

The future pattern of the polecat's recovery in Britain could be influenced in many ways by a range of natural or man-made pressures, some of which have been identified in preceding sections of this report. The polecat is recolonising areas of higher human activity where it faces more threats than exist in its historical upland stronghold. On the other hand, where habitat quality is adequate, polecats may benefit from richer prey populations available in the more productive lowlands. There is still limited understanding of how the balance between these conflicting forces might promote or hinder the polecat's encouraging recovery, though the species' faltering status in Europe is telling. In this section ten important issues are identified, and 23 recommendations (presented as bullet points below) are made for addressing these through research, monitoring and conservation action. Many of these recommendations will be acted upon by the VWT and its collaborators. In order to present these issues briefly and clearly, references to the published literature have not been inserted in this section. Instead, sections of this report where referenced discussion can be found are identified.

9.2 Polecat conservation issues

9.2.1 Status in Europe

The polecat's uncertain status in much of Europe, combined with evidence of recent declines in some countries (see Section 4.3), is a cause for concern. There is a need to place knowledge of the polecat's status in Britain in a European context. There is also need to revise the taxonomic status of European populations.

- A state by state review of the polecat's status throughout its European range, and the conservation issues believed to be affecting it, should be carried out and published. This could be done as a desk study based on consultations with expert mammalogists in each country.

- The taxonomic status of European populations, not studied since the 1930s, should be revised following DNA and morphological studies.

9.2.2 Habitat quality

Evidence from continental Europe suggests that general degradation of habitats, and drainage of wetlands in particular, have affected polecat populations adversely (see Section 4.3). On intensive farmland in Britain the limited extent of semi-natural habitat and poor prey availability must, therefore, be a serious constraint on the species.

- Research should be carried out on variations in the performance of polecat populations in different landscapes, through field studies and population modelling.

131

- The results of such research should be used to guide the development of policies to improve degraded agricultural landscapes in ways that benefit polecats and other wildlife.

9.2.3 Dependence upon rabbits

The rabbit provides the bulk of both food and resting sites for the polecat on lowland farmland according to the VWT study (see Section 8.4.1). In the absence of healthy populations of alternative prey, especially on intensively managed farmland, thriving wild rabbit populations may be critically important for polecat conservation. They may serve to limit competition between the polecat and an ecologically similar introduced species, the American mink.

- Healthy wild rabbit populations should be maintained on farmland in Britain.

- It is accepted that control of rabbits is essential to protect certain economic interests in the countryside. However, in view of the polecat's special dependence upon this species, new control techniques should ideally be approved only if they can be shown to pose no significant threat to the conservation status of the polecat.

- Since some existing rabbit control techniques such as burrow fumigation ('gassing') are likely to be lethal to polecats, alternative methods should be promoted by advisory agencies in areas where polecats are known to occur.

9.2.4 Secondary poisoning with rodenticides

There is growing evidence of the risks to polecats associated with predation upon farmyard rodents contaminated with anticoagulant rodenticides (see Section 8.4.2). A significant proportion of the polecat population is exposed to such poisons and an unknown proportion die as a result. The effects of such toxins upon populations are unknown. Current monitoring of this poisoning through the Wildlife Incident Investigation Scheme is not believed to be adequate. There are concerns about the implications for polecat recovery of the much heavier use of rodenticides in the east of England, beyond the current limits of the species' range.

- Improved monitoring of background rodenticide exposure levels should be undertaken by screening the livers of road casualty polecats that have lived through the main mid-winter period of rodenticide use.

- Research should be undertaken to identify the lethal doses, sub-lethal effects and metabolism characteristics in polecats of widely-used rodenticides.

- An assessment of the population effects of rodenticide poisoning in polecats should be undertaken.

- An assessment of geographical variations in exposure patterns should be carried out (this is being addressed through a collaborative ITE/VWT study).

- Prior to approval, new rodenticide products should be subject to a thorough assessment of the toxicological risk they pose to polecats and other predatory species.

9.2.5 Legal protection

The legality of unlicensed trapping requires clarification (see Section 4.4). Polecats are commonly caught and killed in non-specific tunnel traps (see Section 8.3.12). Many trappers believe that this form of 'accidental' culling is acceptable, despite a legal requirement to take reasonable steps to avoid it (see Section 5.4.2). The polecat is spreading into areas of heavier trapping pressure where there is a greater likelihood of adverse but avoidable effects upon populations.

- The adoption, by users of tunnel traps within or near the polecat's range, of custom-built polecat exclusion devices (developed and tested by the GCT) should be actively promoted.

- Conservation organisations, licensing authorities and bodies representing game shooting and gamekeeping interests should seek to agree and publicise a code of conduct regarding the trapping of polecats. This should state clearly the legal position regarding the use of exclusion devices and the accidental killing of polecats.

9.2.6 Effects of road casualties

The polecat is very vulnerable to road traffic, and there is evidence that this form of mortality has significant effects upon populations where traffic densities are high (see Sections 5.4.2 and 6.4.3).

- Research should be carried out on the effects of busy roads upon polecat populations in Britain. At what density does the main road network prevent the establishment of self-sustaining populations? What proportion of Britain might be unsuitable for polecats as a result? What barriers to dispersal can be identified? What mitigation measures, if any, could alleviate such effects?

9.2.7 Interactions with ferrets

Research described in this report (see Section 7) indicates that introgression with ferrets, though apparent in much of the polecat's range, is not currently a serious cause for conservation concern, except in two reintroduced populations in Cumbria and Argyll. However, the polecat's recovery in Britain is still at an early stage, so monitoring of the pattern of introgression over time would be prudent.

- A further period of widespread, structured sampling of polecats, feral ferrets and introgressive hybrids should be carried out in the first decade of the new millennium and at ten-year intervals thereafter. These new collections of material should be used for morphometric assessment of the relationship between polecats and ferrets.

- Microsatellite DNA fingerprinting techniques should be applied to the above studies of genetic variation in polecats and ferrets.

9.2.8 Distribution-mapping

The polecat's distribution in Britain is likely to continue changing in the new millennium. Active distribution-mapping is essential as a means to plot and understand such changes (see Section 5).

- A further, structured phase of active polecat distribution-mapping should be carried out in the middle of the first decade of the new millennium and at ten-year intervals thereafter. These surveys should be based mainly on the collection of road casualties which can be used in the morphometric studies proposed in Section 9.2.7.

9.2.9 Monitoring changes in abundance

Distribution-mapping cannot be expected to provide information on changes in the abundance of polecats within their main range. Such changes can be important indicators of conservation problems. It is important to study these changes by monitoring (see Section 6).

- The abundance of polecats in Britain should be monitored by sampling at ten-year intervals. The VWT live-trapping system described in Section 6 could form the basis for monitoring throughout the polecat's main range. The next period of monitoring should start in the middle of the first decade of the new millennium.

9.2.10 Raising public awareness

Awareness and appreciation of the polecat and its recovery are limited when compared with birds of prey and some mammals in Britain such as the otter (see Section 4.2). Indifference, ignorance and widespread confusion with ferrets or hybrids are no basis for polecat conservation in the long-term. Moreover, the threat of intolerance and persecution is ever-present in the case of a carnivore with an unsavoury historical reputation.

- Efforts should continue to be made through the media to publicise the polecat's recovery as a conservation 'good news' story at the fringes of its range. In conjunction with other organisations the VWT has used this approach successfully in the English Midlands.

- A general pamphlet about polecats (already published by the VWT) should be distributed widely to raise awareness, especially among the naturalist community. The VWT plans to produce a further pamphlet illustrating the key morphological differences between polecats, ferrets and their hybrids. Production of a slide pack on polecat conservation and ecology would further aid the dissemination of knowledge. This material could be distributed to Wildlife Trusts, County Museums and Mammal Recorders.

- Advice should be promoted about the effective protection of penned game and poultry against polecat predation. Rather than lethal control, this should suggest techniques for exclusion of polecats from pens by sound husbandry.

- Public awareness of the polecat would be enhanced by more widespread, sympathetic and accurate representation of the species in popular culture. From tea towels to childrens' story books, there are many artistic and literary opportunities to reinstate the polecat as the familiar native mammal it once was.

10. REFERENCES

ABERNETHY, K. (1994). The establishment of a hybrid zone between red and sika deer (genus *Cervus*). Molecular Ecology 3: 551-562.

AEBISCHER, N.J. & ROBERTSON, P.A. (1992). Practical aspects of compositional analysis as applied to pheasant habitat utilization. In: I.G. Priede & S.M. Swift (eds) Wildlife Telemetry: Remote Monitoring and Tracking of Animals, Ellis Horwood Ltd., Chichester, pp. 285-293.

AEBISCHER, N.J., ROBERTSON, P.A. & KENWARD, R.E. (1993). Compositional analysis of habitat use from animal radio-tracking data. Ecology, 74, 1313-1325.

ALDISS, B. (1995). Shy beasts who share our cities. The European Magazine, 7-13 July 1995.

ANON. (1984). Nature Conservation in Great Britain. Nature Conservancy Council, Peterborough.

ANON. (1989). Guidelines for the selection of biological SSSIs. Nature Conservancy Council, Peterborough.

ANON. (1993). Biodiversity Challenge - an agenda for conservation in the UK. RSPB, Sandy.

ANON. (1995). Biodiversity: The UK Steering Group Report. HMSO, London.

ANON. (1998). UK Biodiversity Group, Tranche 2 Action Plans. English Nature, Peterborough.

ARNOLD, H.R. (1978). Provisional atlas of the mammals of the British Isles. Institute of Terrestrial Ecology, Abbots Ripton.

ARNOLD, H.R. (1984). Distribution maps of the mammals of the British Isles. Institute of Terrestrial Ecology, Abbots Ripton.

ARNOLD, H.R. (1993). Atlas of Mammals in Britain. Institute of Terrestrial Ecology, Abbots Ripton.

ASHTON, E.H. (1955). Some characters of the skulls and skins of the European polecat, the Asiatic polecat, and the domestic ferret (Addendum). Proceedings of the Zoological Society of London 125: 807-809.

ASHTON, E.H. & THOMSON, A.P.D. (1955). Some characters of the skulls and skins of the European polecat, the Asiatic polecat, and the domestic ferret. Proceedings of the Zoological Society of London 125: 317-333.

BAGHLI, A., ENGEL, E. & VERHAGEN, R. (1998). Premières données sur la répartition et le statut des mustélidés en général et du putois (*Mustela putorius* L.) en particulier au Luxembourg. Bull. Soc. Nat. Luxemb. 99: 87-93.

BAILEY, R.C. & BYRNES, J. (1990). A new old method for assessing measurement error in both univariate and multivariate morphometric studies. Systematic Zoology 39: 124-130.

BALHARRY, D. & DANIELS, M. (1997). Wild living cats in Scotland. Scottish Natural Heritage Research, Survey and Monitoring Report. No. 23. Edinburgh.

BALHARRY, E., STAINES, B.W., MARQUISS, M. & KRUUK, H. (1994). Hybridisation in British Mammals. JNCC Report No. 154. Joint Nature Conservation Committee, Peterborough.

BELL, D.J. & WEBB, N.J. (1991). Effects of climate on reproduction in the European wild rabbit *(Oryctolagus cuniculus)*. Journal of Zoology, London 224: 639-648.

BIRKS, J. (1990). Feral mink and nature conservation. British Wildlife, 1: 313-323.

BIRKS, J. (1992). Searching for County polecats. Warwickshire Wildlife No. 81, p.13. Warwickshire Nature Conservation Trust Magazine, Coventry.

BIRKS, J. (1993). The Return of The Polecat. British Wildlife, 5, (1): 16-25.

BIRKS, J. (1994). The march of the polecat. The Countryman, 99 (1), Winter 1994. Burford.

BIRKS, J. (1995). Wild about rats. Country Life, August 31st 1995. London.

BIRKS, J. (1996). The rise of the polecat. Natural World, Autumn 1996. 26-28. RSNC, Lincoln.

BIRKS, J.D.S. (1997). A volunteer-based system for sampling variations in the abundance of polecats *(Mustela putorius)*. Journal of Zoology 243: 857-863.

BIRKS, J.D.S. (1998). Secondary rodenticide poisoning risk arising from winter farmyard use by the European Polecat *Mustela putorius*. Biological Conservation 85, 233-240.

BIRKS, J.D.S. (in press). The recovery of the polecat *(Mustela putorius)* in Britain. In Griffiths H.I. (ed.) Mustelids in a modern world. Proceedings of the mustelid session of the Euro-American Mammal Congress, Santiago De Compostela, Spain, July 1998. University of Hull Press.

BLANCO, J.C. & GONZALEZ, J.L. (1992). Libro rojo de los Vertebrados de España. ICONA, Madrid. 714pp.

BLANDFORD, P.R.S. (1986). Behavioural Ecology of the Polecat in Wales. Unpubl. PhD. thesis. University of Exeter.

BLANDFORD, P.R.S. (1987). Biology of the Polecat *Mustela putorius:* a literature review. Mammal Review 17 (4): 155-198.

BLANDFORD, P.R.S. & WALTON, K.C. (1991a). Polecat *Mustela putorius*. In: G.B. Corbett & S. Harris (eds) The Handbook of British mammals, 3rd edition, pp. 396-405. Oxford: Blackwell Scientific Publications.

BLANDFORD, P.R.S. & WALTON, K.C. (1991b). Ferret, *Mustela furo*. In: G.B. Corbett & S. Harris (eds) The Handbook of British mammals, 3rd edition, pp. 405-406. Oxford: Blackwell Scientific Publications.

136

BREITENMOSER, U. (1998). Large predators in the Alps: the fall and rise of man's competitors. Biological Conservation, 83 (3): 279-289.

BROWN, D. (1989). Bele'r Coed. Arolwg 1987 Y canlyniadau. Nature Conservancy Council, Bangor.

BROWN, R.W., LAWRENCE, M.J. & POPE, J. (1984). The Country Life Guide to Animals of Britain and Europe. Country Life Books.

BUCHALCZYK, T. & RUPRECHT, A.L. (1977). Skull variability of *Mustela putorius* Linnaeus, 1758. Acta Theriologica 22(5): 87-120.

BURTON, R. (1993). Nature note. Weekend Telegraph, 30th January 1993. London.

CHANIN, P.R.F. (1976). The ecology of feral mink (*Mustela vison* Schreber) in Devon. PhD. thesis, University of Exeter.

CHANIN, P.R.F. & JEFFERIES, D.J. (1978). The decline of the otter *Lutra lutra* L. in Britain: an analysis of hunting records and discussion of causes. Biological Journal of the Linnean Society, 10: 305-328.

CHAPMAN, N., HARRIS, S. & STANFORD, A. (1994). Reeves' Muntjac *Muntiacus reevesi* in Britain: their history, spread, habitat selection, and the role of human intervention in accelerating their dispersal. Mammal Review 24 (3): 113-160.

CLARKE, G.P., WHITE, P.C.L. & HARRIS, S. (1998). Effects of roads on badger *Meles meles* populations in south-west England. Biological Conservation 86: 117-124.

CLUTTON-BROCK, J. (1981). Domesticated animals from early times. London: British Museum (Natural History).

CLUTTON-BROCK, J., KITCHENER, A.C. & LYNCH, J.M. (1994). Changes in the skull morphology of the Arctic wolf, *Canis lupus arctos*, during the twentieth century. Journal of Zoology, London 233: 19-36.

CONDRY, W.M. (1991). The Natural History of Wales. Bloomsbury Books, London.

CORBET, G.B. (1971). Provisional distribution maps of British mammals. Mammal Review 1 (4/5): 95-142.

CORBET, G.B. (1978). The mammals of the Palaearctic region: A taxonomic review. London: British Museum (Natural History).

CRAIK, J.C.A. & BROWN, D. (1997). Polecats in the West of Scotland. Glasgow Naturalist 23 (2): 50-53.

CRESSWELL, P., HARRIS, S. & JEFFERIES, D.J. (1990). The history, distribution, status and habitat requirements of the badger in Britain. Nature Conservancy Council, Peterborough.

CROSS, A.V. & DAVIS, P.E. (1998). The Red Kites of Wales. The Welsh Kite Trust, Llandrindod Wells.

DADD, M.N. (1970). Overlap of variation in British and European mammal populations. Symposium of the Zoological Society of London 26: 117-125.

DAVIES, J. & PORTER, M. (1993). Country Matters. The Daily Mail, 6th November 1993. London.

DAVISON, A., BIRKS, J.D.S., GRIFFITHS, H.I., KITCHENER, A.C., BIGGINS, D. & BUTLIN, R.K. (1998). Hybridization and the phylogenetic relationship between polecats and domestic ferrets in Britain. Biological Conservation. 87 (2): 155-162. **[NB this paper was published in 1998, but was incorrectly referenced as 1999 by the publisher]**.

DAVISON, A., BIRKS, J.D.S., MARAN, T., MACDONALD, D.W., SIDOROVICH, V., GRIFFITHS, H.I. & BUTLIN, R.K. (in press). Conservation implications of hybridization between polecats, ferrets and European mink (*Mustela* sp.). In Griffiths, H.I. (ed.) Mustelids in a modern world. Proceedings of the mustelid session of the Euro-American Mammal Congress, Santiago De Compostela, Spain, July 1998. University of Hull Press.

DAY, M.G. (1966). Identification of hair and feather remains in the gut and faeces of stoats and weasels. Journal of Zoology, London, 155: 485-497.

DEPARTMENT OF THE ENVIRONMENT, TRANSPORT AND THE REGIONS, (1997). Transport statistics, Great Britain 1997. London: The Stationery Office.

DUNN, P. (1994). Never mind the smell, welcome a friend home. The Observer, 11th December 1994. London.

EDWARDS, R. (1997). Furry subversives undermine Britain's railways. New Scientist 153, no. 2072: 6.

EIBERLE, K. (1969). Vom Iltis (*Mustela putorius*) in der Schweiz. Schweizerische Zeitschrift für Forswesen 120 (2): 99-107.

ELLERMAN, J.R. & MORRISON-SCOTT, T.C.S. (1951). A check list of Palaearctic and Indian mammals. London: British Museum (Natural History).

FEWINS, C. (1995). On the scent of a suspected serial killer. Weekend Telegraph, 18th March 1995. London.

FERNÁNDEZ, C. (1993). Effect of the viral haemorrhagic pneumonia of the wild rabbit on the diet and breeding success of the golden eagle *Aquila chrysaëtos* (L.). Rev. Ecol. Terre Vie 48: 323-329.

FLACK, K. (1994). Persecuted Polecat returns. Wildlife Guardian 29, Autumn 1994.

FORREST, H.E. (1907). The Vertebrate Fauna of North Wales. Witherby, London.

FORREST, H.E. (1921). Polecats in Shropshire and North Wales. Naturalist 1921: 286.

FORREST, H.E. (1923). Increase of polecats. Naturalist 1923: 18.

FULLER, H.E., CHASEY, D., LUCAS, M.H. & GIBBENS, J.C. (1993). Rabbit haemor-rhagic disease in the United Kingdom. Veterinary Record 133: 611-613.

GATES, T. (1998). After a century in limbo polecats are coming back. Farmers' Weekly, 27 March 1998.

GUY, J. (1995). Pyne. Julia MacRae Books, London.

HARRIS, S., CRESSWELL, W.J., FORDE, P.G., TREWHELLA, W.J., WOOLLARD, T. & WRAY, S. (1990). Home-range analysis using radio-tracking data - a review of problems and techniques particularly as applied to the study of mammals. Mammal Review, 20 (2/3): 97-123.

HARRIS, S., MORRIS, P., WRAY, S. & YALDEN, D. (1995). A review of British mammals: population estimates and conservation status of British mammals other than cetaceans. Joint Nature Conservation Committee, Peterborough.

HEMMER, H. (1990). Domestication. The decline of environmental appreciation. Cambridge: Cambridge University Press.

HEPTNER, V.G. (1964). Über die morphologischen und geographischen Beziehungen zwischen *Mustela putorius* und *Mustela eversmannii*. Zeitschrift für Säugetierkunde 29: 321-330.

HEPTNER, V.G. (1966). Über die geographische Variabilität und die Nomenklatur der Ilitise. Zoologischer Anzeiger 176: 1-3.

HOLLANDER, H. & VAN DER REEST, P. (1994). Red Data Book of Threatened Mammals in the Netherlands. Vereniging voor Zoogdierkunde en Zoogdierbescherming.

HORNSBY, M. (1993). Polecat enjoys smell of success. The Times, November 2nd 1993. London.

HUTCHINGS, M.R. & HARRIS, S. (1996). The current status of the brown hare *(Lepus europaeus)* in Britain. Joint Nature Conservation Committee, Peterborough.

JEFFERIES, D.J. (1992). Polecats *Mustela putorius* and pollutants in Wales. Lutra 35: 28-39.

JENSEN, A. & JENSEN, B. (1972). The polecat (*Putorius putorius*) in Denmark. Dansk Vildtundersfgelser, 18: 1-32.

JOHNSTON, J.L. (1999). A naturalist's Shetland, London: Poyser.

JONES, P. (1992a). An assessment of the feasibility of re-introducing the polecat (*Mustela putorius*) into populated rural areas of England, with special reference to Dartmoor. Unpublished BSc. Honours project. Seal-Hayne College.

JONES, P. (1992b). A survey of attitudes towards the polecat in Britain. Unpublished report to English Nature.

JORDAN, D. (1997). Hampshire Mammal Report 1997.

KENWARD, R. (1987). Wildlife Radio Tagging: Equipment, Field Techniques and Data Analysis. Academic Press, London.

KITCHENER, A. (1995). Wildcats. The Mammal Society, London.

KITCHENER, A.C. (1998). The Scottish wildcat - a cat with an identity crisis? British Wildlife 9 (4): 232-242.

KREBS, J.R. (1997). Bovine Tuberculosis in Cattle and Badgers. Ministry of Agriculture, Fisheries and Food, London.

KRUSKA, D. (1988). Mammalian domestication and its effect on brain structure and behavior. In: H.J. Jerison & I. Jerison (eds) Intelligence and evolutionary biology. pp. 211-250. NATO A.S.I. Series Vol.G.17. Springer, Berlin.

KRUSKA, D. (1996). The effect of domestication on brain size and composition in the mink (*Mustela vison*). Journal of Zoology, London 239: 645-661.

LANGLEY, P.J.W. & YALDEN, D.W. (1977). The decline of the rarer carnivores in Great Britain during the nineteenth century. Mammal Review 7 (3/4): 95-116.

LAWRENCE, M.J. & BROWN, R.W. (1973). Mammals of Britain. Blandford Press, Poole.

LIBOIS, R. (1984). Atlas des Mammifières de Wallonie, le genre *Mustela* en Belgique. Cahiers Éthologie Appliquée, 4: 281-287.

LODÉ, T. (1994). Polymorphisms in the European polecat *Mustela putorius* in France. Small Carnivore Conservation, 11: 10.

LODÉ, T. (1997). Trophic status and feeding habits of the European Polecat *Mustela putorius* L. 1758. Mammal Review, 27 (4): 177-184.

LOVEGROVE, R. (1990). The Kite's Tale: The story of the red kite in Wales. RSPB. Sandy, 147 pp.

LYNCH, J.M. (1995). Conservation implications of hybridisation between mustelids and their domesticated counterparts: The example of Polecats and feral Ferrets in Britain. Small Carnivore Conservation, 13: 17-18.

LYNCH, J.M & HAYDEN, T.J. (1995). Genetic influences on cranial form: Variation among ranch and feral American mink *Mustela vison* (Mammalia: Mustelidae). Biological Journal of the Linnaean Society 55: 293-307.

MACDONALD, D.W., MACE, G. & RUSHTON, S. (1998). Proposals for future monitoring of British mammals. Department of the Environment, Transport and the Regions. London.

MASON, C.F. & WEBER, D. (1990). Organochlorine Residues and Heavy Metals in Kidneys of Polecats *(Mustela putorius)* from Switzerland. Bull. Environ. Contam. Toxicol. 45: 689-696.

MATHESON, C. (1932). Changes in the Fauna of Wales within Historic Times. Cardiff.

McDONALD, R.A., HARRIS, S., TURNBULL, G., BROWN, P. & FLETCHER, M. (1998). Anticoagulant rodenticides in stoats (*Mustela erminea* L.) and weasels (*M. nivalis* L.) in England. Environmental Pollution 103: 17-23.

McDONALD, R.A., & HARRIS, S. (in press). The use of trapping records to monitor populations of stoats *Mustela erminea* and weasels *M. nivalis*: the importance of trapping effort. J. Appl. Ecol.

McKAY, J. (1995). Complete guide to ferrets. Swan Hill Press, Shrewsbury.

MICKEVICIUS, E. & BARANAUSKAS, K. (1992). Status, abundance and distribution of mustelids in Lithuania. Small Carnivore Conservation 6: 11-14.

MILLER, G.S. (1912). Catalogue of the mammals of western Europe (exclusive of Russia) in the collections of the British Museum. London: British Museum (Natural History).

MILLER, G.S. (1933). The origin of the ferret. Scottish Naturalist No. 203: 153-154.

MITCHELL-JONES, A.J., AMORI, G., BOGDANOWICZ, W., KRYSTUFEK, B., REIJNDERS, P.J.H., SPITZENBERGER, F., STUBBE, M., VOHRALIK, V. & ZIMA, J. (1999). The Atlas of European Mammals. T. & A.D. Poyser, London.

MOORE, T. (1992). Let slip the cats of war. Weekend Telegraph, 4th January 1992.

MORRIS, P.A. (1993). A red data book for British mammals. The Mammal Society, London.

NAISH, J.W. (1923). Polecats in Radnorshire. Field, October 11th 1923.

NEWTON, I., SHORE, R.F., WYLLIE, I., BIRKS, J.D.S. & DALE, L. (1999). Empirical evidence of side-effects of rodenticides on some predatory birds and mammals. Advances in vertebrate pest management. pp 347-367. In: D.P. Cowan & C.J. Feare (eds). Filander Verlag, Fürth.

NEWTON, I., WYLLIE, I. & FREESTONE, P. (1990). Rodenticides in British Barn Owls. Environmental Pollution, 68: 101-117.

NORBURY, G.L., NORBURY, D.C. & HEYWARD, R.P. (1998). Behavioural responses of two predator species to sudden declines in primary prey. Journal of Wildlife Management, 62 (1): 45-58.

NOVIKOV, G.A. (1962). Carnivorous mammals of the fauna of the USSR. Israel Program for Scientific Translations. Jerusalem.

OLNEY, N.J. & GARTHWAITE, D.G. (1994). Pesticide Usage Survey Report 113: Rodenticide Usage in Great Britain on Farms Growing Grassland and Fodder Crops 1992. MAFF Publications, London.

OWEN, C. (1984). Ferret. In: I.L. Mason, (ed.) Evolution of domesticated mammals. pp. 225-228. Longman, London.

OZOLINS, J. & PILATS, V. (1995). Distribution and status of small and medium-sized carnivores in Latvia. Ann. Zool. Fennici 32: 21-29.

PACKER, J.J. & BIRKS, J.D.S. (1999). An assessment of British farmers' and gamekeepers' experiences, attitudes and practices in relation to the European Polecat *Mustela putorius*. Mammal Review 29: 75-92.

PANAMAN, R. (1992). Reintroduction of Polecat (*Mustela putorius*) and Pine marten (*Martes martes*) in Britain. Small Carnivore Conservation, 6: 20.

PITT, F. (1921). Notes on the genetic behaviour of certain characters in the polecat, ferret and in polecat-ferret hybrids. Journal of Genetics 11: 99-115.

PITT, F. (1923). Polecat in Shropshire. Naturalist, 1923.

POCOCK, R.I. (1932). Ferrets and polecats. Scottish Naturalist No. 196: 97-108.

POCOCK, R.I. (1936). The polecats of the genera *Putorius* and *Vormela* in the British Museum. Proceedings of the Zoological Society of London, 691-723.

POOLE, T.B. (1964). Observations on the facial pattern of the polecat (*Putorius putorius* Linn.). Proceedings of the Zoological Society of London 143: 350-352.

POOLE, T.B. (1966). Aggressive play in polecats. Symposium of the Zoological Society of London, 18, 23-44.

POOLE, T.B. (1972). Some behavioural differences between the European polecat *Mustela putorius*, the ferret, *M. furo*, and their hybrids. Journal of Zoology, London, 166 (1): 25-35.

POOLE T.B. (1978). An analysis of social play in polecats (Mustelidae) with comments on the form and evolutionary history of the open mouth play face. Animal Behaviour, 26 (1): 36-49.

PORTER, V. & BROWN, N. (1997). The complete book of ferrets. Bedford: D & M Publications.

PUGH, H. (1994). Got him collared? Hold your nose. The Independent, 21st January 1994. London.

THE RAY SOCIETY (1969). Watsonian Vice-counties of Great Britain. Publication No. 146. British Museum (Natural History).

REMPE, U. (1970). Morphometrische Untersuchungen an Iltisschädeln zur Klärung der Verwandtschaft von Steppeniltis, Waldiltis und Frettchen. Analyse eines "Grenzenfalles" zwischen Unterart und Art. Zeitschrift für wissenschaftliche Zoologie 180 (3-4): 185-367.

REYNOLDS, J.C. & TAPPER, S.C. (1996). Control of mammalian predators in game management and conservation. Mammal Review 26 (2/3): 127-156.

RICH, T. (1998). Squaring the Circles - bias in distribution maps. British Wildlife, 9 (4): 213-219.

RICHARDSON, J.H., SHORE, R.F., TREWEEK, J.R. & LARKIN, S.B.C. (1997). Are major roads a barrier to small mammals? Journal of Zoology, London. 243: 840-846.

RICHARDSON, P.W. (1995). Polecat - A new county record for this century. Northants Wildlife Trust Newsletter Winter/spring 1994/1995, No. 3.

RITCHIE, J. (1920). The Influence of Man on Animal Life in Scotland: A Study in Faunal Evolution. Cambridge University Press, Cambridge.

SAINT-GIRONS, M.C., MAURIN, H., ROSOUX, R. & KEITH, P. (1993). Les mammifières d'eau douce, leur vie, leurs relations avec l'homme. Ministère de l'agriculture et de la pêche et SFEPM, Paris.

SANTOS REIS, M. (1983). Status and distribution of the Portuguese Mustelids. Acta Zool. Fennica 174: 213-216.

SCHAUENBERG, P. (1969). L'identification du chat forestier d'Europe, *Felis s. silvestris* Schreber 1777, par une méthode ostéometrique. Revue Suisse Zoologie 76: 433-441.

SHEAIL, J. (1971). Rabbits and their history. Newton Abbott: David & Charles 226 pp.

SHIELDS, C. (1993). Woodland Wildlife Appointments Calender. World Wide Fund for Nature, London.

SHORE, R.F., BIRKS, J.D.S., FREESTONE, P. & KITCHENER, A.C. (1996). Second-generation rodenticides and polecats (*Mustela putorius*) in Britain. Environmental Pollution 91 (3): 279-282.

SHORE, R.F., BIRKS, J.D.S. & FREESTONE, P. (in press 1999). Exposure of non-target vertebrates to second-generation rodenticides in Britain, with particular reference to the polecat *Mustela putorius*. New Zealand Journal of Ecology 23.

SIDOROVICH, V.E. (1994). How to identify the tracks of the European mink (*Mustela lutreola*), the American mink (*M. vison*) and the Polecat (*M. putorius*) on waterbodies. IUCN Small Carnivore Conservation Newsletter 10: pp8-9.

SIMPSON, J.A. & WEINER, E.S.C. (1989). The Oxford English Dictionary (Second Edition). Vol XII, p20. Clarendon Press, Oxford.

SKINNER, C., SKINNER, P. & HARRIS, S. (1991). An analysis of some of the factors affecting the current distribution of Badger *Meles meles* setts in Essex. Mammal Review 21 (2): 51-66.

SLATER, F. (1994). Wildlife Road Casualties. British Wildlife 5 (4): 214-221.

SLEEMAN, P. (1989). Stoats and weasels, polecats and pine martens. Whittet Books Ltd., London.

STRACHAN, R. & JEFFERIES, D.J. (1996). Otter Survey of England 1991-1994. The Vincent Wildlife Trust. London.

STUBBE, M. & STUBBE, A. (1994). Säugetierarten und deren feldökologische Erforschung im östlichen Deutschland. Tiere im Konflikt 3, 52. Martin-Luther-Universität Halle-Wittenberg.

SUMPTION, K.J. & FLOWERDEW, J.R. (1985). The ecological effects of the decline in Rabbits (*Oryctolagus cuniculus* L.) due to myxomatosis. Mammal Review, 15 (4): 151-186.

TACK, C. (1995). Bedfordshire Mammal Report. Bedfordshire Naturalist for 1994, 49 (1): 23.

TAPPER, S. (1992). Game Heritage, Game Conservancy Ltd., Fordingbridge.

TAYLOR, W.L. (1952). The polecat (*Mustela putorius*) in Wales. J. Anim. Ecol. 21: 272-274.

TEALL, N. (1982). A Natural Survivor? The polecat in Britain. Country Life, December 9th 1982.

TEERINK, B.J. (1991). Hair of Western European mammals: atlas and identification key. Cambridge University Press.

TETLEY, H. (1939). On the British polecats. Proceedings of the Zoological Society of London 109B: 37-39.

TETLEY, H. (1945). Notes on British polecats and ferrets. Proceedings of the Zoological Society of London 115: 212-217.

THOMSON, A.P.D. (1951). A history of the ferret. Journal of the History of Medicine and Allied Sciences 6(4): 471-480.

TROUT, R.C. (1994). Don't let rabbits beet your profits down to the ground. British Sugar Beet Review 62 (1): 30-33.

TROUT, R.C., TAPPER, S.C. & HARRADINE, J. (1986). Recent trends in the rabbit population in Britain. Mammal Review 16: 117-123.

TROUT, R.C. & TITTENSOR, A.M. (1989). Can predators regulate wild Rabbit *Oryctolagus cuniculus* population density in England and Wales? Mammal Review 19 (4): 153-173.

TROUT, R.C., CHASEY, D. & SHARP, G. (1997). Seroepidemiology of rabbit haemorrhagic disease (RHD) in wild rabbits (*Oryctolagus cuniculus*) in the United Kingdom. Journal of Zoology, London, 243: 846-853.

TUBBS, C.R. (1997). Man's vertebrate competitors. British Wildlife, 8 (4): 205-212.

VIGNA TAGLIANTI, A. (1988). Stato attuale delle conoscenze sulla biologica e la conservazione dei Carnivori in Italia. Suppl. Ric. Biol. Selvaggina *XIV*: 401-417.

VILLAFUERTE, R., CALVETE, C., GORTÁZAR, C. & MORENO, S. (1994). First epizootic of rabbit haemorrhagic disease in free living populations of *Oryctolagus cuniculus* at Doñana National Park, Spain. J. Wildl. Dis. 30: 176-179.

VILLAFUERTE, R., LUCO, D.F., GORTÁZER, C. & BLANCO J.C. (1996). Effect on red fox litter size and diet after rabbit haemorrhagic disease in north-eastern Spain. Journal of Zoology, London 240: 764-767.

VOLOBUEV, V.T., TERNOVSKII, D.V. & GRAFODATSKII, A.S. (1974). The taxonomic status of the white African polecat or ferret in the light of karyological data. Zoologicheskii Zhurnal 53: 1738-1740.

WALTON, K.C. (1964). The distribution of the polecat (*Putorius putorius*) in England, Wales and Scotland, 1959-62. Proceedings of the Zoological Society of London, 143: 333-336.

WALTON, K.C. (1968a). Studies on the biology of the polecat *Putorius putorius* (L.). Unpubl. MSc. thesis, University of Durham.

WALTON, K.C. (1968b). The distribution of the polecat, *Putorius putorius*, in Great Britain, 1963-67. Journal of Zoology, London, 155 (2): 237-240.

WALTON, K.C. (1970). The polecat in Wales. In: W.S. Lacey, (ed.) Welsh Wildlife in Trust. North Wales Wildlife Trust, Bangor. pp. 98-108.

WALTON, K.C. (1977). Polecat. In: G.B. Corbet & H.N. Southern (eds) The Handbook of British Mammals, 2nd edition. Blackwell Scientific Publications, Oxford. pp. 345-352.

WEBER, D. (1988). Die aktuelle Verbreitung des Iltisses (*Mustela putorius* L.) in der Schweiz. Revue suisse Zool. 95 (4): 1041-1056.

WEBER, D. (1989). The ecological significance of resting sites and the seasonal habitat change in polecats (*Mustela putorius*). Journal of Zoology, London, 217: 629-638.

WIGAN, M. (1992). Playing God with wildlife. The Field, March 1992.

WILCOX, P.M. (1978). MAFF Pest Infestation Control Laboratory Report. Ministry of Agriculture, Fisheries and Food, Llandrindod Wells.

WILSON, G., HARRIS, S. & McLAREN, G. (1997). Changes in the British badger population, 1988 to 1997. People's Trust for Endangered Species, London.

WISE, M.H., LINN, I.J. & KENNEDY, C.R. (1981). A comparison of the feeding biology of mink *Mustela vison* and otter *Lutra lutra*. Journal of Zoology, 195: 181-213.

WOLSAN, M. (1993). *Mustela putorius* Linnaeus 1758; Wald Iltis, Europäischer Iltis, Iltis. In: Niethammer, J. & Krapp, F. (eds.). Handbuch der Säugetiere Europas Vol.5, part 2. pp. 699-769. Wiesbaden: Aula.

WOODS, M. (1993). The polecat's return. Financial Times, 15th May 1993. London.

YALDEN, D.W. (1986). Opportunities for reintroducing British Mammals. Mammal Review 16 (2): 53-63.

YALDEN, D.W. (1993). The problems of reintroducing carnivores. Symposia of the Zoological Society of London, 65: 289-306.

11. APPENDICES

Appendix 1. A summary by county of the extinction, re-establishment and current status of the polecat in Britain (to aid comparison, the order and nomenclature of counties follows Langley & Yalden, 1977).

County	Extinction date (after Langley & Yalden, 1977)	Status in 1997	Probable re-entry period, if applicable	Additional comments
ENGLAND				
Kent	c. 1870	Still absent.	-	
Surrey	1890-1900	Still absent.	-	
Sussex	1890-1900	Still absent.	-	
London	c. 1825	Still absent.	-	
Middlesex	1850-1870	Still absent.	-	
Essex	c. 1860	Still absent.	-	Recolonisation from Hertfordshire likely in the near future.
Berkshire	?	Re-established in parts.	mid 1990s	First confirmed record from near Kingston Bagpuize in 1995. Population probably derived from reintroduction.
Hampshire	1890-1900	Re-established in the west and the south. Expanding?	Early 1990s	Probably reintroduced at more than one location. First confirmed record near Ringwood in 1994.
Dorset	1890-1900	Possibly re-established in the east, following spread from Hampshire?	Mid-1990s?	Unconfirmed records from near Wimborne Minster from 1996 onwards.
Somerset	1900-1910	Still absent.	-	
Devon	1887	Still absent.	-	
Cornwall	c. 1890	Still absent.	-	
Suffolk	1900-1910	Still absent.	-	
Norfolk	1900-1910	Still absent.	-	
Cambridgeshire	c. 1905	Still absent? (see below).	-	Recolonisation from Bedfordshire/ Hertfordshire likely in near future.
Huntingdonshire	c. 1900	Small population re-established on current Northamptonshire/ Cambridgeshire border between Duddington and Wansford.	mid-1990s	Origins unknown, possibly reintroduced. First confirmed record from near Duddington in 1996.

County	Extinction date (after Langley & Yalden, 1977)	Status in 1997	Probable re-entry period, if applicable	Additional comments
Bedfordshire	c. 1900	Re-established in the far south.	Early 1990s	Apparently recolonising the county from reintroduced Hertfordshire population. First confirmed record near Woburn in 1994.
Hertfordshire	c. 1900	Re-established in the centre and the west.	1980s	Reintroduced in 1982 Expanding slowly?
Buckinghamshire	c. 1900	Re-established on the Chilterns in the west.	Late 1980s?	Probably reintroduced. First confirmed record from near Aylesbury in 1990; specimen in Aylesbury Museum.
Oxfordshire	1890-1900	Re-established in the west through natural spread, and in the east through probable reintroduction?	Early 1990s?	First confirmed record 1993.
Wiltshire	1890-1900	Re-established in the north through natural spread, and in the south-east through probable reintroduction to Hampshire?	Mid-1990s	First confirmed record from near Tidworth in 1995.
Gloucestershire	c. 1900	Well-established in the north; scarce or absent from Stroud southwards.	1950-1964	Re-establishment in north-west of the county confirmed by Walton (1964).
Lincolnshire	c. 1904	Still absent.	-	
Northamptonshire	1890-1900	Re-established in the west and possibly in the north-east of the county.	1980s?	Recolonised from Warwickshire to the west. First confirmed record from Byfield, 1994. Probably genuine records from 1980s not accepted at the time (P. Richardson, pers. comm.).
Rutland	1900-1910	Still absent.	-	
Leicestershire	c. 1890	Re-establishing in far west?	Mid-1990s	Recolonised from Warwickshire to the west. First confirmed record from near Wibtoft, 1994 (specimen in Leicester City Museum).

County	Extinction date (after Langley & Yalden, 1977)	Status in 1997	Probable re-entry period, if applicable	Additional comments
Warwickshire	1892	Well-established and increasingly widespread.	1970s?	First confirmed record from near Alcester, 1992 (mounted specimen owned by Mr. John Jones of Great Alne). Probably genuine records from 1970s not accepted at the time (P. Copson, pers. comm.).
Worcestershire	c. 1900	Well-established and widespread.	1960s	Record from 1968 confirmed by Walton (1970).
Herefordshire	Never extinct	Well-established and widespread.	-	
Shropshire	Never extinct	Well-established and widespread.	-	
Nottinghamshire	c. 1900	Still absent.	-	
Derbyshire	1900	Re-establishing in the far south-west, following spread from Staffordshire.	Early 1990s	First confirmed record from near Church Broughton, 1993. Mounted specimen in Derby City Museum.
Staffordshire	1892	Re-established and increasingly widespread.	Late 1970s?	Game Conservancy records from county in early 1980s (Tapper, 1992).
Cheshire	1900	Re-established and increasingly widespread.	Early 1970s?	Game Conservancy records from county in early 1980s (Tapper, 1992).
Yorkshire	1910	Still absent?	-	Likely to be recolonised soon by eastward expansion of reintroduced Cumbrian population.
Lancashire	1900-1910	Re-establishing in the far north following southward expansion of reintroduced Cumbrian population.	Mid-1990s	First confirmed record from near Kirkby Lonsdale, 1995.
Durham	1890	Re-establishing?	Mid-1990s	Unconfirmed records from mid-1990s; confirmed specimen from near Staindrop, 1998.

County	Extinction date (after Langley & Yalden, 1977)	Status in 1997	Probable re-entry period, if applicable	Additional comments
Northumberland	c. 1910	Re-establishing in the far west following eastward expansion of reintroduced Cumbrian population.	Mid-1990s	First confirmed record from near Haltwhistle, 1997.
Westmorland	c. 1910	Re-established following reintroductions; increasingly widespread.	Reintroduced late 1970s	Many early specimens showed evidence of hybridisation with ferrets. Most 1990s specimens appear pure.
Cumberland	c. 1915	Re-established following reintroductions to Westmorland; increasingly widespread.	Late 1980s?	First confirmed record from near Penrith, 1993.

WALES

County	Extinction date	Status in 1997	Probable re-entry period	Additional comments
Monmouthshire	c. 1900	Re-established in parts, but absent or unrecorded in at least five 10km squares.	1940s?	Records from 1947-1950 (Taylor, 1952); confirmed records from 1959-62 (Walton, 1964).
Glamorganshire	c. 1900	Re-established in parts, but apparently still absent from most of the county.	1950s	One confirmed record for 1959-1962 (Walton, 1964); further records from 1976 onwards (Arnold, 1978).
Carmarthenshire	Never extinct	Well-established and widespread following recolonisation from the north of the county.	-	Restricted to north of county in early 1960s (Walton, 1964).
Pembrokeshire	Never extinct	Well-established and widespread.	-	Very scarce in 1959-1962 (Walton, 1964), but recolonised subsequently (Walton, 1968b).
Breconshire	Never extinct	Well-established and widespread.	-	Confined to north of county in early 1960s (Walton, 1964).
Cardiganshire	Never extinct	Well-established and widespread.	-	Part of the species' historical stronghold.
Radnorshire	Never extinct	Well-established and widespread.	-	Part of the species' historical stronghold.

Appendix 1 continued

149

County	Extinction date (after Langley & Yalden, 1977)	Status in 1997	Probable re-entry period, if applicable	Additional comments
Montgomeryshire	Never extinct	Well-established and widespread.	-	Part of the species' historical stronghold.
Merionethshire	Never extinct	Well-established and widespread.	-	Part of the species' historical stronghold.
Flintshire	c. 1910	Well-established and widespread.	1940-1962	One record for 1959-62 (Walton, 1964).
Denbighshire	Never extinct	Well-established and widespread.	-	Confined to south-west in 1959-1962 (Walton, 1964).
Caernarvonshire	Never extinct	Well-established and widespread.	-	Part of the species' historical stronghold.
Anglesey	c. 1910	Currently re-establishing.	Mid-1990s	First confirmed record from Plas Coch, 1996 (K. Walton, pers. comm.).

SCOTLAND

County	Extinction date (after Langley & Yalden, 1977)	Status in 1997	Probable re-entry period, if applicable	Additional comments
Roxburghshire	1880	Still absent.	-	Likely to be recolonised in near future from the south, via expansion of reintroduced Cumbrian population.
Berwickshire	1880	Still absent.	-	
Selkirkshire	1850-1880	Still absent.	-	
Dumfriesshire	1867	Still absent.	-	Likely to be recolonised in near future from the south, via expansion of reintroduced Cumbrian population.
Kirkcudbrightshire	1880	Still absent.	-	
Wigtownshire	c. 1880	Still absent.	-	
East Lothian	c. 1860	Still absent.	-	
Midlothian	c. 1855	Still absent.	-	
West Lothian	1870-1880	Still absent.	-	
Peebleshire	1850-1880	Still absent.	-	
Lanarkshire	c. 1855	Still absent.	-	
Ayrshire	c. 1882	Still absent.	-	
Fife	1880	Still absent.	-	

Appendix 1 continued

County	Extinction date (after Langley & Yalden, 1977)	Status in 1997	Probable re-entry period, if applicable	Additional comments
Kinross-shire	1870-1880	Still absent.	-	
Clackmannanshire	1850-1880	Still absent.	-	
Stirlingshire	1879	Still absent.	-	
Dunbartonshire	c. 1870	Still absent.	-	
Renfrewshire	c. 1868	Still absent.	-	
Angus (Forfar)	c. 1860	Still absent.	-	
Perthshire	1904	Still absent?	-	Reported reintroductions in early 1990s; no confirmed specimens recovered.
Argyllshire	1900-1915	Re-established following reintroductions.	1970s	Reintroduced from 1970 onwards. First confirmed records from 1987 onwards (Craik & Brown, 1997).
Kincardinshire	1851	Still absent.	-	
Aberdeenshire	1890	Still absent.	-	
Banffshire	1867	Still absent.	-	
Morayshire	1870-1880	Still absent.	-	
Nairnshire	1870-1880	Still absent.	-	
Inverness-shire	1900-1915	Still absent.	-	
Ross and Cromarty	1900-1915	Still absent.	-	
Sutherland	1910-1920	Still absent.	-	
Caithness	c. 1890	Still absent?	-	Unconfirmed reports from the A9 north of Helmsdale.

Appendix 2. Latin names of species mentioned in the text.

Rabbit	*Oryctolagus cuniculus*
Brown hare	*Lepus europaeus*
Grey squirrel	*Sciurus carolinensis*
Bank vole	*Clethrionomys glareolus*
Field vole	*Microtus agrestis*
Water vole	*Arvicola terrestris*
Wood mouse	*Apodemus sylvaticus*
Common rat	*Rattus norvegicus*
Wolf	*Canis lupus*
Husky dog	*Canis familiaris*
Red fox	*Vulpes vulpes*
Pine marten	*Martes martes*
Stoat	*Mustela erminea*
Weasel	*Mustela nivalis*
Siberian, eastern or steppe polecat	*Mustela eversmannii*
European polecat	*Mustela putorius*
Black-footed ferret	*Mustela nigripes*
Feral ferret	*Mustela furo*
Feral American mink	*Mustela vison*
European mink	*Mustela lutreola*
Badger	*Meles meles*
Otter	*Lutra lutra*
Feral cat	*Felis catus*
Wildcat	*Felis silvestris*
Leopard	*Panthera pardus*
Red deer	*Cervus elaphus*
Sika deer	*Cervus nippon*
Reeves' muntjac	*Muntiacus reevesi*
Golden eagle	*Aquila chrysaëtos*
Common buzzard	*Buteo buteo*
Red kite	*Milvus milvus*
Pheasant	*Phasianus colchicus*
Hedgehog tick	*Ixodes hexagonus*